At last, one of the great un
has been researched and t
readable tale. A

Jim Reynolds
Independent Motorcycle Journalist

An enjoyable unputdownable book.
In fact - a spiffing read!

Roger Gwynn
Draganfly Motorcycles

A fascinating tale that very few people have heard of,
brought to vivid life by this new book.
A rollicking adventure - and true into the bargain!

Peter Henshaw
ex-Editor of MotorCycle Sport

The facts have been melded into a gripping story
which all flows in a very readable manner.

Graham Austin
MCC, MSCC

Enormously interesting!

Dr. Robert Poole
Historian

THE SIX DAY AFFAIR

SALZBVRGER
FESTSPIELE

THE SIX DAY AFFAIR

John Bradshaw

PUBLISHING

THE SIX DAY AFFAIR
© J.R.Bradshaw 2014

Published by JRB Publishing
Malvern, September 2014

ISBN 978-0-9566403-7-6

Apple Macs	OSX
Adobe InDesign	CS6

Titles & Subtitles	**Gill Sans Bold**
Present Tense, 3rd Person	Gill Sans, unjustified
Past Tense, 1st Person	Garamond, justified
Past Tense, 3rd Person	Garamond, justified & indented

Designed by **JRB**   john@jrbpub.net

Printed & Bound in Great Britain
by **Aspect Design**, Malvern   www.aspect-design.net

for **JRB Publishing**   www.jrbpub.net

CONTENTS

INTRODUCTION   11

Main Map   12

CHAPTER 0 - in which Eric thinks back   15
CHAPTER 1 - in which the ISDT is explained   17
CHAPTER 2 - in which we learn what Eric didn't know   27
CHAPTER 3 - in which we meet some fellow travellers   35
CHAPTER 4 - in which other events are discussed   43
CHAPTER 5 - in which they experience a bit of Culture   57
CHAPTER 6 - in which Eric's team-mate finally arrives   61
CHAPTER 7 - in which the Trial starts   69
CHAPTER 8 - in which the day fails to go as expected   87
CHAPTER 9 - in which Austria's scenery is appreciated   95
CHAPTER 10 - in which most British riders leave   111
CHAPTER 11 - in which a dash for home is made   123
CHAPTER 12 - in which there is further trouble   139
CHAPTER 13 - in which good fortune lends a hand   147
CHAPTER 14 - in which the party heads further West   151
CHAPTER 15 - in which it all comes to an end   159
CHAPTER 16 - in which a few loose ends are tied up   171

AUTHOR'S NOTES   179

DRAMATIS PERSONÆ   183

ACKNOWLEDGEMENTS & THANKS   193

REFERENCES   195

Austria's new Governor, Baldur von Schirach, gave a speech at the Opening Ceremony of the Salzburg Festival, culminating with "In Mozart's name, we call the young to arms".

"The biggest experience of the first day had been that loose gravel doesn't have the same frictional coefficient as a nice new rough asphalt surface. The English private riders lost a whole clutch of men, but ... (they) were more or less unknown people, who may not have been aware what a six day's trial in Germany's high mountains stands for!"
Das Motorrad September 1939

"This ISDT has generated a new 'technical phrase', coming from Otto Sensburg, our national rider. When our riders had gone into hedges or onto the ground, they would say 'Da hat's mi überlistet!' [There it did outwit me!] That is a pretty figurative saying because the first day it did outwit many riders and this always happens at the beginning of an ISDT, as one does not find ones' 'speed' straight away..."
Das Motorrad September 1939

Baron von Falkenhyn was most upset (to hear they were leaving) but nevertheless produced a last bottle of champagne to toast the spirit of motorcycling comradeship ... although the Baron may have been smarting over the £1 he had bet Graham Walker that there would be no war between Germany and Britain...

"Let us hope that peace will prevail and that the 1940 event will take place under happier auspices."
Motor Cycling September 1939

INTRODUCTION

Perhaps unconventionally, despite dealing as accurately as possible with factual events of 75 years ago, this book nevertheless takes the form of starting most chapters with a very old man, Eric, talking to his grandson, Andy, in the present day.

However, despite this adventure tale being presented as merely the memories of an old man, none of the actual names, facts or chronologies have been changed in any way at all. Only plausible interpolations and extrapolations have been made, so attempting to avoid any significant misrepresentation of the real history.

Occasional asides have been interjected, which are entirely factual, in order to supplement what would otherwise be just how one man remembered the events.

At the end, there are some very brief accounts of what actually happened afterwards to just a few of those involved. If more information could be obtained, any possible future editions could include it.

The Author's Notes at the back disentangle fact from fiction in greater detail.

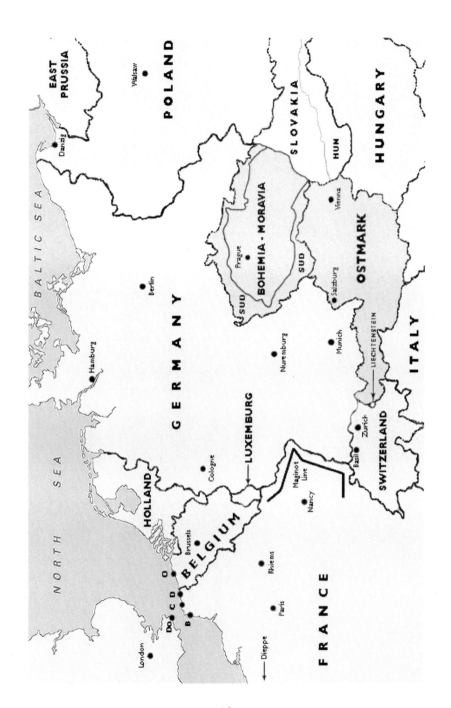

KEY to MAIN MAP

The Map approximately represents the Country Borders by August 1939, with late additions to the 'Greater German Reich' shown shaded.

The annexation and control of Sudetenland, the western border regions of Czechoslovakia occupied by many German people, took place in Octber 1938. It is labelled **SUD** on the map, while the area of southern Slovakia subsequently occupied by Hungary is labelled **HUN.**

After the Nazi occupation of more of Czechoslovakia in March 1939, the 'protectorate' was split into 'Bohemia-Moravia' in the west and 'Slovakia' in the east, with parts shared out to the USSR.

Upon the annexation of Austria, or the 'Anschluss Österreichs', in March 1938, reinforced by an apparently supportive plebicite shortly afterwards, the Nazi government re-labelled Austria as 'Ostmark', or the 'Eastern Marches', re-using a medieval name for the Saxon or later Bavarian area east of the Elbe River.

Relevant Channel Ports are labelled as:

B	Bologne
C	Calais
Do	Dover
D	Dunkirk
O	Ostend

CHAPTER 0

- in which Eric thinks back

"CENTENARY? It can't be – I mean it was only a few years ago when they were all shouting about the 50th Anniversary of the Inter." Eric is talking quite loudly with one of his grandson's discarded bike magazines on his lap, although he's entirely on his own in the house apart from the cat, which is not impressed - nor very interested come to that.

"Yes, that was in…er…the Sixties it must have been. So that means …ah. Oh well, alright, a hundred years then, but then it was a long time ago when we were there. Watching it all in Wales was great fun, with Dick and Arthur and Gustav too, but then the next year, in Germany, now that was really something…" and in his head Eric drifts back well over seventy years, his eyes closing and the rocking chair echoing the increasing pace of the story as he re-lives it once more in his mind.

Her grip around my waist suddenly tightened and I felt her knees squeeze my hips – well, she was hanging on all right. I'd already ducked forward and tucked my elbows in. Leaving it in first gear, I snapped the throttle grip back and hung on. The Scott responded enthusiastically as always, the yowl of its exhaust increasing as we accelerated hard, down and away from the Swiss Border Post.

We could no longer hear the guards' yells, but expected to hear what came next. The sharp cracks from behind us confirmed that there were bullets whizzing overhead. Closing the throttle only slightly and easing the clutch, I snicked it into second and opened wide again. We were already up to 45, heading for 60mph and up another gear. Thankfully the road was clear, with a reasonably good surface, although Lavinda on the pillion was having to take her weight off the seat by almost standing on the pillion foot-rests - while keeping low at the same time…

"All right?" I shouted over my shoulder.

"Yes. Yes, but…"

CHAPTER I

"**HI GRANDDAD!** How're y'doin'? I got us some sticky buns and... Hey, you OK?" Eric is clearly not with it to start with, but then little does his grandson know that he's dragging the old man back from the distant past.

"Oh - Andy. What are you doing here? Er - ah, it's Saturday, isn't it. Good to see you lad. Have you got any pastries with you by any chance?"

"Yes, of course I've got some 'pastries' as you call 'em. But, were you OK? You seemed a little bit - somewhere else?" Andy knows that his grandfather is already well into his nineties but nevertheless still happily firing on all cylinders most of the time - not that he's quite sure how many cylinders that is...

"Well, I was just thinking about the International that I went to, back before the war. Did I ever tell you about it?"

"International? International what? Rugby? Conference? Baccalaureate? What?"

"No no no, you silly boy, the International Six Days Trial, of course. The Olympics of Motorcycling. Top of the heap. That was the one that only the very best got to ride in, leave alone getting to take a gong home too! Oh yes, the top chaps were there, Vic Brittain on his cammy Norton - he'd got a Gold more than once in the past! And George Rowley on the AJS and that had a cammy engine too, and there was Len Heath on his Ariel - oh and Marjorie Cottle on a Triumph for a change, not the Raleigh she was famous for. There were quite a few BSAs too. Who else? Can't remember just now, but anyway there was only the best there. Did I tell you about it?"

"No, Granddad, I don't think you did. But when was this? Before the war, you said, but when?" Andy is currently between girlfriends and somewhat belatedly taking an interest in motorbikes, to the approval of his grandfather, if not his parents. Fighting his way through the latest version of the Government's expensive obstacle course, clearly designed to discourage motorcycling, he is meanwhile fascinated by his grandfather's previously hidden history.

"Oh, it was in 1939, August it was, or was it September? No, it was towards the end of August and jolly hot it was too over there in Germany. I tell you, the weather was..." but Andy interrupts him.

"What? In Germany? In September 1939? But - but that's when the war started, wasn't it? I mean, it was only on the first of September that Germany bombarded Danzig for heavens sake - and you were in Germany? You weren't there really, were you?"

"Oh I don't know about Danzig - but I suppose you do, don't you lad? You got that degree in history or something, didn't you? Oh yes, you'll know all about it I suppose."

"A European History degree at Aberystwyth, actually. But no, I sure don't know all about it! So, go on - tell me what happened." Andy settles down into the settee - and then jumps back up again. "No, hang on Gramps - I'll make a pot of tea and we'll have those buns while you tell me. OK?"

So Eric collects his thoughts, ready to start again from the beginning...

Saturday 12th August, 1939

The cross channel ferry was heaving as it headed east and I was really feeling rather queasy.... I have to admit that it was the first time that I'd ever been to sea. Oh, I'd been in boats, but this was a bit different. I mean, it was all a bit different right from the start, with them pumping my petrol tank out and then not even paying for it! And then roping my beautiful Scott with their great greasy slings and hoisting it way up over the dock and then down out of sight! I didn't see it again until they manhandled it back out again in Boulogne. But it was alright, I suppose. It survived. But then, on the docks, they tried to sell me petrol at stupid prices! Bastards.

Anyway, apart from all the rolling about - and the expensive gnat's piss they fobbed us off with instead of any real beer - it was quite fun on the boat. The ferry, that is. Malcolm kept telling us it was a ship, not a boat, and he knew because he was in the Merchant Navy - but then he didn't make it through in the end, did he... What a shame - I liked Malcolm, despite everything. I'd met him that afternoon, waiting at the docks. He was on a BSA outfit and it was he who introduced me to Connor, who was also riding a Beeza - a solo 350. I'd seen it on the docks and very neat it was too - made my roadster 600 Flyer look rather overweight!

Connor's was a proper competition piece, no messing, and he was a good type too, including me in their group straight away, which was good because I was feeling very much on my own. I didn't know anybody really, as Graham hadn't turned up and most of the party were experienced, serious competition riders. In fact, some of them I knew already - well, knew about anyway. I didn't know them to talk to, but I'd read all about them in the Green-Un. Len Heath and Vic Brittain, oh and Jefferies too - they were there, but then they'd been heroes of mine since I was a lad and I wasn't going to just walk up and natter to them! Oh no. They were on quite a different plane, if in the same bar.

"So who are you with then, Eric?" Connor had sat down with Malcolm and me, balanced on a stool with a mug of cocoa in one hand and a collection of biscuits in the other. Clearly he thought I was crew for one of the competitors - which I was, sort of...

"Well, I'm supposed to be passengering for Graham Oates, but he hasn't turned up. There's more ferries yet, so he'll probably make it."

"Oates? He rides with the South Liverpool Club doesn't he - on an Ariel? Yes, I remember, usually on a bigger-banger - a cracking good Red Hunter it was – and he does well on it, eh?"

"Well yes, he's usually on a works RH500, but this time they've got him to ride an outfit again. He rode a Squariel in the International last year, but the sidecar chassis broke and he had to retire. Bloody annoyed he was too!"

"So why's he back on another outfit then?" interjected Malcolm, looking genuinely puzzled. "I mean, if he does so well on the solo 500 singles, why go back to having a chair to slow him down? 'Specially if it breaks!"

"Oh, it's what the factory wanted, wasn't it. He who pays the piper calls the tune. They launched their new push-rod Square Four last year, the 1000, and wanted lots of good publicity. But he didn't finish of course, so I suppose they're trying again."

"I know the one - saw it at Olympia. Looks fine for a sidecar tug I'm sure. The 4G, isn't it?" Connor dunked another biscuit into his drink.

"Well, that's not quite what he's riding this time" I replied, and started to explain. "What he's being set up with is the new 4H and..." when one of the others came over and butted in.

"Another bevvy will ya Con? Oh - what's that? Coffee? Wassa matter wi' you then? Gone saft on us 'ave yer?"

"No, Gerry, I've not gone soft and it's not coffee, it's cocoa. And yes, I'd like another one please." He handed the empty mug to the now wordless Gerry with a polite smile.

"Right. A cocoa. Right..." and he took it and slowly walked away, sadly shaking his head. As he disappeared around the bar we all burst out laughing, when just at that point a lady came round the bar in the opposite direction.

"Hello Miriam - come and join us." We all moved round a bit and Connor dragged a chair across. "You know Malcolm of course, but - er, oh dear. Tell me your name again? I'm sorry..."

"Eric. Eric Dale. Hello Miriam." I'd already stood up and offered her my hand, which she brushed, smiling as she sat down. She really was very lady-like, a mousey blonde, quite tall, but unassuming, and at the time it was hard to imagine her riding a bike - but a couple of days later I knew better.

"Eric - of course. Memory like a sieve! Anyway, Eric, may I introduce you to Mrs Miriam Anning, pilot of a very sporting little mudplugger, masquerading as a BSA Empire Star roadster." Con was doing his best, and covering up the embarrassment well - not that he needed to as he was a really nice fellow. In any case I suppose I wasn't paying him much attention by then really as he had just been eclipsed by this reserved but clearly personable newcomer. But I was young and shy, whereas she was a fair bit older than me and obviously much more well known and important, so I just kept quiet. Anyway, they were talking about who was on board and who wasn't, and how the others were getting there.

I remember Malcolm telling us that most of the Civil Service team – the CSMA or the 'pen-pushers' as Malcolm called them - were coming by road, not by train. As he said, the government weren't going to pay for nice new machines or train tickets for them just to come over for a holiday! But at the time none of us knew quite how they were going to do it, although this didn't stop Malcolm telling us about it anyway.

"Fred Perks will sort it out - he's always in charge and knows what to do. And thank goodness he's behind all those clueless MPs is what I say!" and Malcolm laughed at his own wit, or what he thought passed for it. "They're all on BSAs, just like us, y'know. The Right Crowd, that's us, eh?"

He looked round the bar, which was fairly empty at that point, and twirled his non-existant mustache, pretending to be one of the Brooklands Boys. "The right crowd and no crowding, what?" His wit knew no bounds it seemed, even on weak foreign beer.

"Well, I suppose that doesn't include me then?" I said.

"What? Why not? Oh - I see. So what are you riding then?" Whilst I'd parked my bike close to their BSAs back on the dock, Malcolm hadn't connected it with me of course.

"Oh, he's got a posh bike he has!" said Connor, smiling. He must have seen me park it earlier on. "It's a Scott - nothing common like a Beesa!" Malcolm's eyebrows lifted at this, but he didn't reply immediately. He was on his third pint and, although it was pretty thin tasteless stuff, I don't think he'd had anything to eat for ages so it was having an effect.

"Oh! A Scott, eh? Which one?" he finally responded.

"It's a Flying Squirrel, the 600." I wasn't comfortable about where they'd got me by then. I mean, yes, the Flyer was an expensive bike, much more than a 350 BSA certainly. Dad had bought it for my 21st earlier that year. Oh, not new, but it looked it - it really was a lovely machine and I'd polished before setting out the previous day. "I don't know about 'posh'...... it's the rather heavy version I'm afraid."

"I saw a roadster Scott parked on the quay. You're not competing on it then?" Miriam asked, raising an eyebrow.

"Oh no! Goodness no, not on the Scott!" - but then Malcolm chipped in yet again.

"Don't you listen to him! He's Oates' TSR, he is. Too modest is our Eric. A behind-the-scenes acrobatic grease monkey, nothing less." It was good of him to try to build me up, but then it was up to a rather different status than I'd previously thought - whatever a 'TSR' was?
But then Miriam made it clear.

"Ah, a traveling support rider are you? - well, you'll be busy in the coming couple of weeks then!" and Miriam smiled at me. I probably blushed. I can't remember, but certainly for a short time I felt almost proud with an official label: a 'TSR' sounded so much better than just 'passenger'. But then I thought about what she'd just said: "..you'll be busy.." Well, I suppose so, but just what had I let myself in for? Graham hadn't mentioned anything about TSRs and whatever else that involved...

"Well, Graham wanted a passenger and as I was coming over anyway he said that I'd do, but I don't know if I'll be..." I started to explain – and petered out.

"Oh you'll be in good hands, don't you worry - if Graham can't handle an outfit I don't know who can. After all, he usually prefers to ride on his own anyway, so you'll probably just be ballast. So don't worry - just hang on! But yes, you'll be busy." The others nodded in agreement and I was just a little relieved and even encouraged.

"Votre cacao, monsieur. Est-ce que quelque chose est exigé, mesdames et messieurs?" Connor accepted the drink and turned to us.

"Looks like Gerry has bottled out! Anyone else want anything?" We all declined and he turned back to the waiter. "Aucun, merci," passing him a Francs note, before getting back to his attempted inventory.

"So, we're all here and I've seen Vic, oh and Geoff too - he's with Fred Neill who's managing the AMC teams this year. Malc's told us about the CSMA wallas - but what else do we know?" He looked around at us - but I for one knew nothing of course. "Ah, Miriam - where's Marjorie? Is she hiding herself shyly away in a cabin somewhere below?"

"Oh no - she'll be flying in, but her back-up crew is well ahead of her, naturally. Her bike and all the spares have already been shipped over there of course." She was quick was Miriam and this was briefly met with a stunned silence. Then Dave Edda, who'd just joined us, burst out laughing. Blimey, for a moment I'd got completely the wrong end of the stick and thought I was mixing with the Upper Classes under false pretences. Not that I thought that Marjorie Cottle was really in that sort of upper class, but what did I know then?

"Very good." Con had squeezed her arm, smiling broadly. "Now, how's she really getting here?"

"Oh you know Marjie, she'll always do it her own way. Triumph have provided her with a new 250 this year and they're paying her expenses too, up to a point. They'll..." - and Dave cut in.

"But Marjorie rides for Small Heath now, doesn't she?"

"Not this time - BSA dropped out earlier this year and Triumph stepped in very promptly. They'll get good advertising out of it when she does well of course. But Marjie's not one to waste her pennies, so she's running it in on the way over here. Her friend Dorothy will probably be giving it a full oil change and whatever for her when they meet up."

22

"She's riding - all the way there? It's well over 700 miles each way!" Malcolm was staggered - he'd not even considered doing that. "But, who with?"

"Who with? Well not with Dot. No, she's riding there on her own. Marjie likes her own company - not got to wait for anyone that way. Er, I think Dot's on this ferry, somewhere." Well, I was impressed. Oh, I'd read something of Marjorie Cottle's career up 'til then, what with her Round The Coast jaunt, medals in the Scott and MCC trials in the mid-twenties, mostly all on Raleighs, and then her ISDT successes on BSAs more recently. She was clearly a goer and no delicate flower as we'd clearly seen the previous year in Wales, but still looking smart and tidy in the pictures of her in the comics anyway. So I was looking forward to seeing her again that year, maybe even meeting her?

"So she's no longer one of us then, eh?" Malc just couldn't resist it. "What?"

"Not on a Beeza, is she?" His broad smile started to fade as he saw his latest witticism had fallen on stoney ground.

There seemed to be little more news available about other competitors' travel arrangements at that point and the conversation went on to how mutual friends - and others - had been doing in the season so far, and what sponsorships might be up for grabs. This was all beyond my ken and I seem to remember I was sagging a little by then anyway, so I took my leave and went off to find somewhere for a bit of a kip.

There were always several awards up for grabs at the ISDTs. As well as the premier awards, that's the International Trophy and the Silver Vase, there were also the Hühnlein, the Bowmaker and the Manufacturers' Trophies. The team members worked together for these awards whilst also hoping for an individual Gold, Silver or Bronze medal. The Bowmaker catered for clubs, whereas the trophy awarded by Adolf Hühnlein, who was in overall charge of the event in 1939, was mainly aimed at military and para-military teams, including police and similar organisations of which the Germans had entered 27, in contrast to just 7 British teams. The A-CU organised the two National teams and in May 1939 sent out invitations for the programme of selection tests which were to take place the following June.

So, competing for the Hühnlein Trophy were the CSMA team, two A-CU teams, three War Office teams and one from the Sunbeam MCC. The latter in particular comprised of three very experienced riders, two men and a woman, with an equally experienced team manager, Fred Neill.
In both 1928 and '29, Neill was in the British teams that won the ISDT International Trophy and by 1939 he was the team manager for the AMC riders as well as the SMCC team of Cottle, Ford and Saunders. Marjorie Cottle had been in the only all women team to ever win the ISDT Silver Vase Trophy, eleven years earlier. Geoff Godber-Ford had gained an ISDT Gold in 1938, while Alan Saunders was a successful trials rider who also carried on competing after the war.

The CSMA team comprised of similarly experienced riders: Fred Perks, Les Ridgeway and Fred Whitehouse. Perks had gained an ISDT Gold in 1937 and had been doing equally well in 1938 until he was caused to crash by another competitor. In addition, Norman Blockley was with them as their TSR, while his brother Tim was riding a BSA for the A-CU and Sunbeam MCC teams, the latter competing for the Bowmaker Trophy.
The CSMA riders were all mounted on 500 BSAs, although the competitors' machines were very new, being M23 and M24 Gold Stars. Whitehouse and Ridgeway rode the 496cc M24 machines with alloy engines, as did those in the Army's Team A, while Perks rode a 496cc M23 iron engined machine. The bikes effectively being developmental, BSA Works Manager Bert Perrigo accompanied the War Office teams, while keeping an eye on the CSMA riders too.

The team travelled to Germany in different ways, Ridgeway travelling by train. Whitehouse rode all the way, carrying his BSA on the chassis of his Ariel outfit. Perks drove in his 1937 Standard Flying Nine saloon car, having removed the rear seats in order to fit in his dismantled BSA. Whitehouse and Perks went in convoy with Harold Tozer, a member of the BSA team. Tozer's car towed a trailer which carried his 500 BSA and sidecar, while Tom Davies, the BSA Team Manager, also travelled in the car. The convoy crossed by ferry from Dover to Ostende, then travelled to Brussels, where Perks was amused to spot a poster in the window of the local BSA agent proclaiming his recent win in the Victory Cup Trial.

The group temporarily split up and when Perks and Whitehouse got to Trier they found that the banks had closed, so they had no Reichmarks. They nevertheless booked into a hotel and were escorted to a bank the following morning, with the hotel manager perched on the Ariel's pillion seat. They also had problems finding petrol, with almost every pump displaying '𝓛𝓮𝓮𝓻' or '𝓐𝓾𝓼𝓿𝓮𝓻𝓴𝓪𝓾𝓯𝓽' - empty or sold out. However, by using the fuel stored in Perks' recently acquired 10 litre jerry-can and in the tanks of the bikes being carried on the trailers, they made it through Munich and on to more plentiful supplies.

They later found Tozer and Davies picnicing by the roadside and so they all finally arrived in Salzburg together, not too far behind those who had travelled by train.

Ridgeway, Perks and Whitehouse

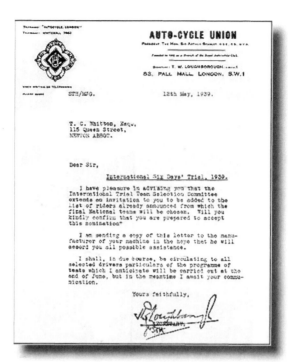

The letter sent by the A-CU to Tom Whitton in May 1939

Dear Sir,

I have pleasure in advising you that the ISDT Selection Committee extends an invitation to you to be added to the list of riders already announced from which the final National teams will be chosen. Will you kindly confirm that you are prepared to accept this nomination?

I am sending a copy of this letter to the manufacturer of your machine in the hope that he will accord you of all possible assistance.

I shall, in due course, be circulating to all selected drivers particulars of the programme of tests which I anticipate will be carried out at the end of June, but in the meantime I await your communication.

Yours faithfully,
(signed) T. W. Loughborough
SECRETARY

In the event, Whitton was not selected for a National team, and rode his AJS 350 for the West of England MCC, competing for the Bowmaker Trophy.

CHAPTER 2

- in which we learn what Eric didn't know

"Y'KNOW LAD, it's strange, but I didn't ever find out just how all of the others did get there, although I heard a few tales and there were lots of different ways of doing it, or so they said..." and Eric chuckles to himself as he thinks of it.

"But I suppose we didn't really know what was going on back then anyway and so I never heard about all of it. Well, not 'til long afterwards anyway, through the grapevine back in England - oh, and in the papers and the magazines too of course, the Blue 'Un and the Green 'Un, they covered it a bit. But not all of it though, I'm sure..."

What was unknown to many of the competitors was that the British Government, in the light of the rapidly developing European situation, had initially advised the A-CU (Auto-Cycle Union, the organising body for British competitors) not to go over to Germany to take part in that year's ISDT.

However, it was nevertheless widely known that central Europe seemed to be in a rather unstable state, certainly as far as anything to do with the National Socialist German Workers Party was concerned, which by then was totally dominating Germany. Up until about the Spring of 1939 though, it was seen by many in Britain to be merely a Central European affair. There was some awareness of issues such as Chancellor Hitler's drive for Lebensraum (living space) which apparently involved re-gaining 'lost territories', or gaining new land where there were significant numbers of people of German origin. Ostensibly this was building on the 19th century Volksdeutsche or pan-germanismus movement (the unity of all German-speaking peoples). Even less clear for very many at the time was the extremists' commitment to 'racial purity' and the growing campaign against the Jews and Romani.

The well established rules of the FICM (Fédération Internationale Clubs de Motocyclisme, the overall organiser of the ISDT, later to become the FIM) stated that the overall winning nation should host the following year's event.

Britain had won in 1936 and 1937, as well as six times previously, and were used to hosting the event in Wales. Having won again in 1938, the A-CU had naturally been expecting to host the 1939 ISDT again, presumably in Llandrindod Wells once more.

However, quite out of the blue, the FICM changed its rules and declared that no nation should host the event for more than two consecutive years. While this was surprising, it was not necessarily a bad thing as hosting the event involved a great deal of work and was very expensive, so it could have been seen as 'spreading the load'.

 What is more, there had been a high retirement rate and numerous casualties at previous events based around Llandrindod Wells, so the A-CU was probably happy about the change. But who was to host it?

France perhaps, as they had not done so since 1930, or Italy who were keen contenders, having won in 1930 and '31. Sweden, Germany, Switzerland, Austria, Norway, Holland or Belgium were all reasonable possibilities too. In the end, the FICM declared that it should be hosted by Austria and based in Salzburg. However, Hitler's forces had already marched into Austria back in March 1938. Consequently the British Government and the A-CU were a little concerned to find that, with the HQ of the 1939 ISDT being re-located to Salzburg, effectively the event would seem to be held in the new Greater Germany!

The grass-roots motorcyclists were surprised too and there was much discussion and supposition taking place at club nights, especially amongst those who had been at previous years' events. They had seen the escalation of national support for the German teams, especially compared with the early 1930s when their German friends were competing on a similarly amateur basis as the British. By 1937 however, the German riders were all riding German machines which were the very latest competition models directly supplied by the manufacturers. What is more, both the riders and the support teams were required to wear military uniforms, initially mainly Reichswehr (army and navy) but later also Luftwaffe (air force) uniforms too. While some German riders did privately admit that they abhorred the militarisation of their teams, they did of course appreciate all the new machines, equipment and the large scale technical support which contrasted sharply with that of all the other nations that were competing.

But why had all this happened? At least one rider had been taken into confidence one evening over a few beers towards the end of the 1938 event. It seems that Herr Hitler had been made aware of the International Six Days Trial and it had been presented as being the motorcycling equivalent of the Olympics, which of course he regarded as being of great significance, especially after Germany's successes in the 1936 Olympics in Berlin. So unsurprisingly he demanded that Germany should win the major ISDT awards and thereafter dominate the event. This was not an unreasonable aim, as Germany had indeed done very well in 1933, 1934 and 1935, so his demand in 1936 that they should succeed yet again presumably seemed quite achievable, especially if the country's resources were to be substantially put behind its teams.

However, it was all to no avail. In 1936, at Freudenstadt, Britain dominated the event. Just to rub salt into it, they did it again in 1937 at Llandrindod Wells and then once more in 1938, all of which would have been rather unsatisfactory for Adolf. So, what more could be done?

Looking at it over a pint of ale in an English pub, the situation must have seemed quite clear. The FICM had obviously been pressurised behind the scenes to change the rules so that the next year's event did not take place on Britain's home ground yet again.

Not only that, since national boundaries had been rearranged, next time it could take place on Germany's home ground once more, albeit in recently occupied Austria. It was all quite obvious really - if not necessarily entirely true.

Whatever the reasons, in 1939 it was going to all take place in the wonderful countryside and mountains surrounding Salzburg, even if that wasn't quite what had been expected. Any unrest or doubt was presumably still being assuaged by the previous September's Munich Agreement, after which Neville Chamberlain had assured Great Britain of "...peace for our time...", being a direct quote of Benjamin Disraeli when he came back from Berlin in 1878 and misquoting the Book of Common Prayer.

So the A-CU made the necessary preparations to go to Salzburg to compete, sending letters to suitable riders in May inviting them to present themselves at the Selection Trials.

The Selection Trials for the national teams took place in Wales the following June, based at Llandrindod Wells as per usual.

Meanwhile, it seems that the A-CU had not passed on the Government's early advice to the private entries and so there were already just as many individuals and club teams registered for entry as would have been normally expected for such an overseas event. Typically, the British always had a much larger proportion of private entries than did other countries, especially Germany which had very few, but very many military, para-military and works' teams. Italy had even fewer private entries. This tended to reflect the different countries' approaches, the British always being at the amateur and somewhat relaxed end of the spectrum.

Nevertheless, all this still took place despite the German invasion in March of the remaining parts of Czechoslovakia that had not already been occupied. That it was not, after all, just an irrelevant game being played a long way away should at last have been brought home to everybody - and even to preoccupied motorcyclists - by the news on 31st March that Britain and France had decided that they would make a stand if Poland were also to be invaded.

However, at the time it was doubted that this was quite as significant as it seemed and Marjorie Cottle, one of the British competitors, later said that "We all had the feeling that it was the sort of thing that happened to someone else. We went back over to Germany again quite cheerfully, without any thought of Hitler interfering with us."

Certainly Hitler didn't seem to think that there would be any problems. After all, almost exactly a year earlier, Britain had made a similar stand about Czechoslovakia, but then both the British and French Prime Ministers, Chamberlain and Daladier, had backed down, effectively handing the first bits of Czechoslovakia over to Germany and Italy, the Sudetenland being successfully annexed on the 5th October, 1938. So why would it be different this time?

'Not to worry - it'll all sort itself out' was the usual attitude in the clubhouse, and meanwhile, there was the big event for which to prepare, with selection trials for the national teams, factory and club teams to sort out, bikes to be prepared, run in and checked over, leave booked, ferry tickets to buy, passports checked and visas to order - oh, there was plenty to do without worrying about distant political issues as well.

Indeed, it seemed that there was not much to worry about after all because the Foreign Office's latest advice, to the effect that 'the political situation would not become tense', was this time passed on to all by the A-CU. Quite on what basis this advice was given was not made clear, but nevertheless this time all British entrants were told of it by letter. However, competitors were also issued with a copy of an 'Official Letter' to be taken with them, which explained 'To Whom It May Concern' exactly why they were in Germany, clarifying the 'totally non-military nature of the event', and asking that 'special consideration and help' be given to them should there be 'any trouble'. Again, of what value this may have been is now unknown, but what is also unknown is the basis on which the others, the support teams and spectators, presumably all travelled to Germany without copies of the Official Letter.

Nevertheless, along with the A-CU's usual paperwork, there were also 'Notes of Special Advice' for what could be 'unusual circumstances'. For example, it was known that there was at the time much para-military saluting going on in Germany, whereby even civilians in the street or in shops were by then expected to respond to the Nazi salute and "Heil Hitler". After the experience of the 1936 Summer Olympics in Berlin, both the Foreign Office and the A-CU acknowledged that it would almost certainly arise that British Nationals would also be expected to respond to this. The advice was that their response to "Heil Hitler" could instead be a reference to King George VI with "Heil König", or "Long Live The King", possibly also with a British military salute.

The British military salute would of course have been no problem for the three British Army Teams that were competing that year. The ten riders, together with their mechanics, were commanded by Lt.Col.C.V.Bennett and they all went by road, well organised in true military style – despite 'the totally non-military nature of the event'.

The nine army competitors and one reserve had been carefully selected from a short list of over 20 servicemen and then thoroughly trained over the previous months, with special emphasis on the newly introduced scrambles element on the sixth day. The riders underwent weeks of arduous physical and mechanical training. They then rode their machines all the way to Salzburg, comprising a team of three very special BSA 500s, a team of three competition Norton 500s, and a third team made up of three basically standard WD Matchless 350s.

They were backed up with two Army trucks full of spares, supplies and individuals' luggage, while Lt.Col.Bennett led in his Humber Snipe staff car, together with his driver.

However, unlike some of their other motorcycles, the BSA 500s were not standard issue DR's (Dispatch Riders) bikes. In fact, they were three of just twelve very special M24 Gold Stars, sporting alloy heads with hairpin valve springs. Not even the BSA Team had these, although there were also another two M24s and an iron headed M23 in the CSMA team. The Gold Stars had been lent specifically for this event - possibly with an eye on future orders?

Consequently, BSA's Competition Manager, Bert Perrigo, went to keep an eye on them, quite independently of BSA's Team Manager, Tom Davies, who was also at the event.

Members of the three War Office Teams for the 1939 ISDT
No 156 Sgt O. Davies, Matchless 350; No. 113 Pte. J.L. Wood, BSA 500;
No 68 Lt. J. F. Riley, Norton 500; No. 75 Cpl. A.C. Doyle, BSA 500

Bert Perrigo travelled with the Army in his own car and quite appropriately this was a black 1939 BSA Scout, the front-wheel drive Series 6 steel saloon and which was to be the last of the line. While it would have looked very sporting and rather out of place amongst all the khaki painted military vehicles, its 1204cc side-valve engine may in fact have had to work quite hard to keep up with the 4086cc straight-six in the Humber Snipe. Probably it would have been the trucks and the trials motorcycles that would have set the pace though.

The group crossed from Southampton to Bremerhaven, where they were met by a German Major who escorted them in a relay of Wehrmacht vehicles all the way to Salzburg, giving them their first experience of travelling along a new Autobahn.

In retrospect, perhaps the most remarkable aspect of all of this was the fact that, despite their escort, there was actually a detachment of the British Army openly travelling east along a Reichautobahn across the heart of Germany, while back at home their Chiefs of Staff and politicians were contemplating the prospect of imminent war with that very country...

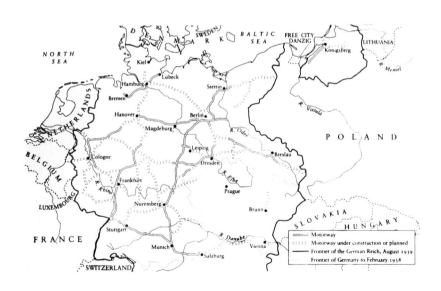

Autobahns existing and under construction in August 1939

33

CHAPTER 3
- in which we meet some of Eric's fellow travellers

"BUT WHAT about your pal - Graham Oates wasn't it?" asks Andy. "Did he make it in time?"

"Oh yes - he did" and Eric laughs even louder this time. "Only just, though. Only just!"

Sunday 13th August, 1939

I was of course very worried about Graham's progress, but had no way to find out how he was getting on. Not until we got off the boat, anyway, but I couldn't be bothered to find a telephone and there was nothing I could have done about it in any case. Meanwhile we had time to kill as the weather was getting no better at all and we had an announcement over the Tannoy that we would have to stand off Boulogne until it abated and we could get into port. Not that I knew what they were on about, but Con translated it for us. We were sitting in the lounge, feeling fed up, although most of us had got used to the ship's motion and the queasiness had worn off.

"Excuse me, but has anyone seen Pat? Pat Gilfinnan, that is. I really can't find him." This made me sit up. The newcomer was a handsome, slim young lady, with her dark brown hair tied up at the back and with her leather helmet firmly in place, which I was later to learn was an almost permanent fixture. As tall as me - but much prettier. Ho, I damn her with faint praise, but really, I was somewhat taken by her looks from the start and so was lost for words. But then, I had never heard of Mr. Gilfinnan before so had nothing to say anyway, I suppose. Neither Con nor Malcolm had seen him either.

"No sign of him recently, Lavinda. Mind you, Pat was knocking back the whiskeys earlier - he may well be asleep!" So possibly he'd passed by and I'd not known.

"Yes. Perhaps. Thanks." And she had gone. Pretty name... That was the first time I met Lavinda. Brief, but memorable.

Oh - I forgot to mention that I'd also met Geoff earlier on. And come to think of it, I later knew that he was pals with Gilfinnan, but I don't remember anybody knocking whiskeys back at that time.

35

So there was Geoff, that's Geoff Godber-Ford of course, with a Sunbeam. We hadn't expected to see him on a 'Beam as he was usually riding either a Royal Enfield or a 250 New-Imperial - although I seem to remember it grew to 350 later on. It was Miriam who'd very briefly introduced me to him and for once I wasn't lost for words. I'd always wanted to meet him after he'd done so well at our local event, the Victory Trial at the Clee Hills, near Cleobury Mortimer where I was born. I knew he was a friendly chap, not at all stuck up like some of the top blokes, so eventually we got to talking. However, the poor old chap had ridden hard to make the ferry and hadn't had any time for a rest, so he'd pushed off soon afterwards.

Later on I'd had a bit of a kip myself and was feeling a bit more perky, so when I saw him sitting further down the lounge I took the opportunity...

"Morning Geoff. A bit brighter now?"

"Oh, hello Eric. Yes, much better thanks - the storm just rocked me to sleep!" He didn't look much better, but then he was tough I suppose. "I'm just getting a coffee - got to get into the continental way of things, y'know! Would you like to join me?"

"Oh - er, yes please." I didn't usually drink coffee, it seemed a bit posh to me back then. Silly, wasn't it? "So, er, are you on your own then?" I'd not identified Geoff's TSR, if he had one.

"Well, I'm in the Sunbeam 'A' Team this year y'know, with Marj and Alan, if that's what you mean?" I knew that the Sunbeam was a club team and wasn't officially supported by the factory, AMC having taken over Marston's Sunbeam a couple of years before.

"No, but what you mean is do I have a support rider?" he went on. "Ha! I prefer to do my own thing. Like Marjie, I usually like to travel on my own – but no, not this time I'll admit. Gil's riding with me on his 350 Ariel." I assumed that he was referring to the elusive Pat Gilfinnan.

"Anyway, apart from him, Marjie's TSR, Dorothy, is very good and I know she'll lend a hand if Alan or I need it." Team member Alan Sanders was riding a Triumph as was Marjorie - but with Geoff on a Sunbeam, Fred Neill from AMC was doubling up as their Team Manager too. There was a lot of good will in those days.

"Con tells me you'll be riding a Sunbeam - what happened to the New Imperial then?"

"Ha! They went bust, didn't they. Right at the last minute - well, last December in fact. I mean, who would have thought it a year ago? Bankrupt! Oh, I know that Jack Sangster's bought it all and they're still just about ticking over, but there's no funds left for competition. But at the time I was tickled pink to be offered a New Imp, even if I did have pay for everything else myself – and the bike really went well too."

"Yes, and I know you rode it last year in the International - we were there, my friends and I, in Wales, and we saw you once. You got a Gold, didn't you?"

"Well, yes I did. But it was a bad do all round in '38 wasn't it, rotten weather and bad going. However, it got me an Imp for the rest of the season though, so it was worth it for me."

"But, what happened? I mean, hey, this is getting rather complicated! New Imp and Sunbeam, alright – but then I remember you winning the Victory Trial on an Enfield in the previous year, so why didn't they take you on?" - but then Geoff was waving his arm up in the air...

"Svp, excusez-moi - café pour deux?"

"Certainement monsieur."

"Right - now, what were you saying? Enfield? Oh yes. Well, not really. But yes, after the Victory Trial, I was loading my own 350 Enfield onto my trailer and a couple of chaps in trench coats and hats came over and said some very nice things to me. It turned out that they were Messrs Bladen and Wilson-Jones, from Royal Enfield. You could have knocked me down with a feather! Anyway, they took my machine away with them back to Redditch, back to the factory - and then returned it to me the very next week with a few more horses tucked away inside! I got to be fifth in the British Experts with that. Great fun, it was. By that time I was getting big ideas and that's when I first fancied myself for the Inter in '38. Not that I'd had any experience of ISDTs by then - I'd not even been to see one! Silly, what?"

"Well, I don't know..."

"No, really I'd got no chance. I mean, there was no way that I could afford it myself as a Private Entrant, and Enfield knew that I'd be just a tyro and so they wouldn't support me - they'd already got Rogers and what's 'isname, Backer was it? No, Booker, Jack Booker. Oh, they knew - and I think those two are riding for Enfield's again this year." He was right - I checked later. "So I gave up on the idea." Our coffee arrived just then.

"Ah, merci. Trente-sept. s'il vous plaît. Merci." And then immediately there was yet another arrival.

"Hi, Peggy. Shift up Eric. Here, have a seat Dot - and a sip of coffee while you're at it - my distemper's gone away for a bit, but there's the other side of the cup just in case. Do you know Eric? Eric, this is Dorothy, she's Marjorie's TSR that I was telling you about. Eric's with Graham Oates - or not, as the fellow hasn't arrived! Any news of him, Eric?"

"No, last I heard he was still playing with gear ratios and visas or something."

"Oh. Mmm. Well, here I am with two TSRs, with both their riders still on the road. Now, I think my Sunbeam's in need of a de-coke, so when you two have finished drinking my coffee, p'haps you'd like to...?" My new compatriot and I swiftly made it clear that we were far too busy.

"But Geoff, if Redditch weren't interested in having you riding one of their Enfields, how come you...?"

"Ah! Now, that's how the grapevine works I suppose. Y'see, at the end of May I received a telegram from Harry Perry - he was the Competition Manager for New Imperial at the time - and it seems that one of his team, I don't know who, had been taken ill and couldn't ride in the Inter, and would I like to take his place? Would I? I jumped at the chance!"

"Wow, I bet you did Geoff. But Perry was with Triumph, wasn't he? Graham has talked about him - they were both riding outfits in the 1933 Inter. Er - Graham was on a Square Four and, oh yes, Perry on a Triumph 6/1, the 650 twin. He must have moved to New Imp after that then." Then Dorothy interrupted.

"But Geoff, Fred told me that you're on a Sunbeam. Are you?" We'd already been through this, but then she'd come in part way through and so was even more confused than me!

"No no, we're talking about last year – '38. But yes, I'm on a 'Beam this year. Anyway, where were we?" He looked at us as if we should know what he was going to say! "Oh yes, I'd bitten off a fair bit more than I expected back then, I can tell you. Would you believe it – New Imp booked me into a five-star hotel in Brum, with all expenses paid at that point! I went to the New Imperial Works in Loveday Street at 9 o'clock every morning for a week. Harry told me that he was supplying me with the latest unit-construction 250cc New Imperial, the crank-case being made out of elektron, which is very light and very expensive! But he said that I was to make myself familiar with every part of it..."

38

He shrugged - "I had to strip a similar engine - not my special one - every day, especially dismantling and re-building the carb and mag."

"Very impressive. But I wonder why they went bankrupt?"

"Oh, that was because Norman Downs died and control of things went to... Eric! That's got nothing to do with it! Where was I? You two keep getting me off the track. Oh yes, stripping. There was no quick-release rear wheel, so if I had a puncture I had to first disconnect the brake linkage, then the chain, remove the two security bolts, fix the puncture and then pump it back up to 18 pounds, before putting the wheel back - and the chain and brake bits too of course. They made me do that three times a day! I'm exhausted even thinking about it - thank goodness my Sunbeam is better equipped. Dunlop have just given us some new anti-puncture solution to put in, but I don't know if it'll work. Anyway, by the end of the week I could do the whole thing in under 8 minutes! I re-fitted the front wheel in under 5 minutes - and that had to go up to 28 psi. Five minutes - good eh?" Geoff smiled, clearly feeling quite pleased with himself, as indeed he had every right.

"And then, in the afternoons, I'd ride through the local lanes, around the cathedral, past Snow Hill Station, all around the small streets with the Head Tester, but, y'know, every day for a week and I can't remember his name! We didn't talk much though, we just rode a lot. Anyway, by the end of the week Harry said he was very pleased with my progress and said that he'd send me the actual machine I was going to ride in the Inter and that I had to carefully run it in myself. He trusted me by then, y'see. So, it arrived on a wagon in the first week of June, all clean and new. Oooh, it was lovely. All shiny it was, with a polished plated tank, not all black like my Enfield - or my 'Beam come to that. Well, my job was to get a few miles on it before taking it back to the factory for the pre-event service, so I got up at about six in the morning and rode it out over the Quantock Hills, near Bridgwater where I live, for about three-quarters of an hour every day. By the end I was going flat out and I really was very pleased with it. It handled really well, especially at speed, but then that summer it was in the high eighties and the tracks over the hills were baked hard. After about 750 miles I returned it, but only got it back about a week before the Trial! However, it had been fully serviced with a new chain and all, and with all the special equipment they thought necessary for the '38 Inter." He paused to drink his coffee, reminding me of mine too.

"They even got me one of those new Barbour jackets! I'm using it again this week - it's really good." We all listened enviously - and not asking if he should have perhaps given it back...

"That was the way to do it, a team of eight of us, full factory support and with Harry there in person to look after us. It's a bit different in the Sunbeam team this year, I must say..." and he sighed sadly. "Anyway, on the Saturday I rode the Imp to the Rock Hotel in Llandrindod Wells, where they had booked me in, and..." His long and detailed account of his former glories was sharply interrupted by an announcement over the Tannoys.

"Attention, s'il vous plaît. Nous accouplerons en quinze minutes. Les passagers de pied satisferont s'attaquent à la sortie aux arcs, et aux automobilistes à la sortie à la poupe. Merci."

"Right - at last! Let's go. Good luck folks" and we all went òff to collect our kit. We filed off down the passengers' ramp - but then had to wait for them to unload our bikes, so Con, Dorothy and I then got to hear the rest of Geoff's tale.

"Where was I?" asked Geoff when we'd all settled down again.

"You were at last year's ISDT in Wales..." said Dorothy, encouragingly.

"Oh yes, well... Well, I did alright really, so they told me they wanted me for this year too. Very nice. Mind you, we thought this was just going to be another re-run back on our home ground yet again, once more showing the Continentals how bikes should be ridden!"

"But Geoff!" interrupted Con, clearly amazed at the way he was telling it. "I mean, you didn't just 'do alright'! C'mon, you…" but Geoff cut him off.

"Yes, yes, I know, but the point was that they offered me it for this year too, but I was playing hard to get because, after '38, I wasn't paying for absolutely everything myself again this time!" He chuckled to himself, while we waited for him to tie all the loose ends together. "I mean, I was in a fairly strong position, because as well as the Inter, at that point I'd also just about got an MCC Triple in the bag. I was riding a 500 AJW-JAP and it had got me Golds in both the Land's End and the Edinburgh that year."

Con chipped in again – he wasn't going to let Geoff understate himself again.

"And you did it too! – you got your third Gold in the London to Exeter trial that December, didn't you! And I know that wasn't a walk-over, because I was on my Beesa and I found it really hard going. It was an awful winter wasn't it. I was soaked but still getting on alright until I made two big footers right near the end, so I only got a Bronze that time."

"Well, that wasn't so bad Con, a Bronze – the Exeter certainly was a tough 'un last year. But yes, I did get my Triple, and as you'll know there weren't many handed out that year - although it didn't do me any good because when I arrived at the New-Imp stand at the Earls Court Show last November I was told that New-Imperial had gone to the wall – liquidised! You could have knocked me down with a feather!" and he held his hands up, clearly remembering the shock of it at the time.

"Bang goes my ride in next year's Inter I thought. But then, out of the blue, good old George – that's George Rowley from AMC – he got in touch and offered me a year's contract! Well, 'Good-bye New-Imperial, hello Associated Motor Cycles' I said to myself. I guess that my luck is just unstable or something? Anyway, they gave me one of their up-rated high-cam 500 Sunbeams on the basis that I'd campaign it in most of the big events through the year – including this year's Inter, so I was back on board – and to prove it, here I am!" He leaned back, folded his arms and smiled at his audience. Well, there were only three of us, but we were all fascinated by his tale.

"Well, come on – what did you do on the 500 then?" Con didn't want that to be the end of his account and in any case they still hadn't unloaded our bikes so we needed something to take our mind off the prolonged wait out in the cold, thin drizzle.

"Oh, there was the Colmore last February where I got the 'Best 500 Cup', then there was the Scottish Six Day Trial of course, that's always an essential one and I did alright there too." Cue for Con to query it and Geoff gave in.

"Oh alright then, I got 'Special First' this year." We were all really impressed by this time, I can tell you. "I had a go at the Victory Trial again and a few more over the following eleven weeks, which brings us right up to date, so you can let go of my collar now Con!" he joked, gently elbowing Con in the ribs as he said it.

However, the dockers still hadn't given us our bikes back and Con wanted still more info.

" Ah, but you're not on the 500 today – I had a look. So what is it?"

"No, true enough, it's a 350 this time, the 347cc 'Beam, but it goes like a 500 I can tell you! Lovely little bus it is – but nowhere to hang my gear, so I've fixed up a couple of rails to hang the panniers and I've got my rucksack too, so I'm alright. Funny really, as they are clearly not pushing the Sunbeams, the AMC aren't. No, I think mine is the only one competing this year. Odd, because it's a fine machine, but probably they're more concerned with the Matchboxes and the AJ's. Someone told me that they're just building them out of the stocks of spares they got from Marstons, with AMC bits where needed, though this one seems genuine enough. Anyway, I can't deny that they've done me well really, they're paying for both my ferry and the petrol. Oh, I've still got to look after my own digs, but it seemed to me to be a fair compromise - and I've always found somewhere to lay my head in the past!"

"Hey – look! At last!" and the first bike, a Norton, could be seen ascending from the ship's hold, swinging out over the dock and then rather too rapidly being lowered down into its owner's worried arms.

Godber-Ford was correct in thinking that AMC were concentrating on their Matchless and AJS marques, eventually reducing them to effectively just one range of badge-engineered models. However, little did he know that AMC was to then sell Sunbeam on to BSA just four years later, in 1943.

After the war, for a short time BSA produced Sunbeam labelled motorcycles, although nothing like the Marston Sunbeams of old. They were designed by Erling Poppe and inspired by the BMW R75 motorcycle that had been supplied to the Wehrmacht during the war.

CHAPTER 4

ERIC IS NOW thinking back to his first time abroad.

"Y'know, I did find it very odd to be riding on the wrong side of the road - but then it was easier on a motorcycle than when we went back to France in the Rover after the war, what with the steering wheel being on the wrong side too, that really was odd. Emily was a real help in the car, though."

"Yes, Grannie was always game for that sort of thing, wasn't she. She had a fair bit of French too, which must have helped. Anyway, getting back to before the war, there you were at the station. You didn't ride to Salzburg then?"

"What? Do you know how far it was? - and still is I expect! It was getting on for 700 miles! No, going there by train was cheaper than using all that petrol and at about half-way we'd have had to stay somewhere overnight too. So going both ways it was cheaper by train - and we could have a kip on board. Quicker too, probably. The bit that really annoys me is that we'd bought return tickets!"

"What's wrong with that then?"

"Well we didn't come back by train, did we? Wasted the bloody ticket!"

"I don't know how you came back, but have you still got the ticket? - you could reclaim the fare perhaps?" Eric turns to look at his grandson as if he's turned a bit simple, but his leg seems to have gone to sleep again, despite having just been pulled.

"Ooooh - I've got to...ah..."

"Here, gimme your arm Granddad - up we go... All right now? D'you feel OK - steady? Want your stick?"

"Aaah, yes. Thanks lad. Perhaps it's time for another cuppa do you think? Meanwhile I'll just go and make room for it", and he heads off to the bathroom.

Settled back into his old armchair, with his gammy leg up on a stool and a fresh cup of tea next to him, Eric gets back to his tale.

Well, they didn't damage my Scott, I've got to give them that, but it took 'em long enough to unload them all - and it was raining! Anyway, we eventually got away and headed for the railway station. I stuck with Con because he could speak the lingo.

Eventually we found Boulogne Railway Station, after being fleeced on the docks for just enough petrol to get us there. Con did his best, but they had us over a barrel, so we had to cough up. We then had to ride round the back and over to the station yard to have the machines loaded onto trucks. The French railway chappies were far more careful with our motorcycles than the dockers had been, but then we were staying right there on the spot until we were happy that they were firmly lashed down and that all was safe and well. They didn't want our tanks drained either.

It was a long train and we walked the length of it before Con found someone who actually knew where our carriage was. Who was there, let's think - there was Con, Gerry, Lavinda, Malcolm, Pat, Geoff, Dorothy, Miriam, er, me, and one or two others I think. Anyway, along we walked and, no surprise, Sod's Law came into action and it turned out that our carriage was all the way behind us, back up at the front, right next to the truck that had our motorcycles in it! It seemed that the great long train would be split up and bits dropped off along its way down into Austria, so we had to be with our machines of course. So we finally found it and all piled in only to find lots of our crowd already there, comfortably settled in. We went along the corridor and found the end compartment vacant so we bagged it. Well, some of us did, but Geoff had spotted Fred Neill and some others in the second compartment and so he, Pat and Dorothy joined them there. Don't know where Gerry got to.

Anyway, Malcolm, Con, Miriam, Lavinda and I settled in and made ourselves comfortable and after what seemed like a very long time there was eventually a lot of shouting and whistle blowing going on outside and we jerked into action.

We relaxed and sat back and watched the French, then eventually the Belgian and before very long after that the German countryside sweep past the window, all very rural and with mostly women working in the fields. Not many men at all so far as we could see. However, while the different countries' fields all looked much the same to us, we could tell the difference because when the train stopped, officials speaking another language would come along to disturb us for our passports and hand us cards with Customs questions in English. All very irritating.

For Geoff and his pals though, going into to Germany wasn't just irritating, it was bloody annoying. They told us later that when we got across the border the uniformed officials were this time accompanied by plain clothes chaps who double-checked our papers - and then confiscated all their newspapers!

Later, it turned out that they were Gestapo, but why they wanted our newspapers and comics I've no idea. They took not only his copy of Lilliput, but Dorothy's Picture Post too and she hadn't even finished reading it! When they got to us they picked up Malcolm's Daily Mirror, but we'd all read it by then and they were welcome to it.

In between interruptions though, it turned out that we had plenty to talk about between us. For some reason the others seemed interested in my cycling activities through Wales and had never even heard of a Dursley-Pedersen bicycle before, but it was Miriam's account of her long-distance trial in 1908 that really interested me. I'd read about it all when I was a boy, never thinking that I'd be in a railway carrage actually talking to the heroine herself! So I plucked up the courage to ask her about it.

"Oh, that was years ago, even before the Great War - you don't want to hear about that do you?" but I assured her that I did! Oh, I didn't know about the others, but they weren't saying anything, so she humoured me.

"Well, we've nothing else to do have we? Oh, why not? Now, when was it - must have been about two years after the Club's President had started the..." she began.

"What club, Miss?" Y'know, Malcolm was a funny chap really. Very deferential to his seniors and to ladies, but never hesitating to butt in. Almost rude he was at times, but Miriam didn't seem to mind.

"Oh, the Motor Cycling Club. THE Motor Cycling Club, not just any motor cycle club y'know. Founded back in 1901 it was, so it's the oldest club of all!"

At this point I wasn't really meaning to follow Malcolm's example, but I'm afraid I did butt in.

"Well, not exactly. I think that the MAC kicked off a few months earlier in fact."

"But it's not a motorcycling club! It's all cars in the MAC!"

"What's the..." but I wasn't waiting for Malcolm at that stage because, while Miriam might have been over twice my age and with far more experience, for some reason I couldn't let it go just then.

"Oh come on, the MCC has cars too - it has done for ages!" I said.

"Well yes, but you can't compare the MAC with the MCC, they're quite..."

"But..." I tried, but Miriam carried on talking right over me.

"...different, they're just a local car club, only interested in sprints and hill climbs and silly games chasing all around Birmingham. Oh, they do have a very nice little hill climb of their own at Shelsley Walsh, but they're still just a parochial bunch of car drivers!"

"Excuse me. Who are you talking about? And what's the em-acey?"

"Malcolm - the M.A.C. is the Midland Automobile Club. Founded in January 1901 in Birmingham." Con had firmly stepped in between us, finally acknowledging Malcolm's puzzlement.

"And I'm a member of the MAC as well as the MCC, so I can tell you that they've got about the same sort of status, but with slightly different interests. Don't you get the wrong impression from these two - I've had just as much fun going up Shelsley as I have up Blue Hills, they're just different, that's all." We looked at each other - and then all laughed.

"Fair enough," I said, "but Miriam, you were beginning to tell us about the 1908 Trial?"

"Oh yes. The President of the MCC two years before, in 1906, was S.F.Edge. Selwyn was a great fellow without a doubt, having won the Gordon Bennett Race, got a Gold in the 1000 mile Trial, and - oh lots of things, so he was a good president right from the start. So, er why was I talking about him....? Ah yes - he got the London to Edinburgh going properly, making it both ways, the 'There & Back Trial' they called it, but it's just called the Edinburgh Trial now of course. And he brought cars in for the first time too.

Oh, it was a full Guinea entry fee for the cars, but we only had to pay half a Guinea to enter on a motorcycle. Mind you, I didn't pay, oh no. Y'see, I can't be a Member. Not of the MCC, it's open to gentlemen only and that really does make me seethe."

This wasn't at all what I expected - she was getting quite worked up about it!

"I mean, Muriel Hind achieved a Gold back in 1906, driving a Deasey car admittedly, but we both got Golds on motorcycles in '08, so we are clearly quite as good as the men!" We could see she was up on her soapbox, but it was indeed all quite amazing, not having really heard much about the club's history before.

"But, now, in the Thirties? You still can't? That's crazy! But, er, but how did you enter then?" Malcolm said it for us.

"My father entered me. A non-member can ride in an MCC event if she, or he, is entered by a Member, and so he did and paid for everything too. He really was a brick, was Father. He'd bought me one of the new Douglas motorcycles, a 350cc machine it was, and I rode that. Muriel rode too, as she was on her motorcycle that time, a Rex as I recall it, and she called it the 'Blue Devil' for some reason, but she was sport - and not shy, oh no. Anyway, we rode together mainly and a cracking good do it was too. The weather was fair that Whitsun and the roads had been pretty dry for some time before so, apart from the dreadful dust, we managed to get along quite well."

"I've read about Miss Hind, I'm sure. She's supposed to have been the first lady in the whole of Britain to own and ride a motorcycle!"

"You're right Malcolm - the first woman in fact!" and Miriam smiled at her own pedantry. "But a lady, certainly, and she did insist on looking quite correct. She always wore her hat held in place with a tulle scarf and, like me, she had an ankle length tweed coat and tall, knee-high lace-up boots, although by the end of the day you really could not tell what colour they had started out as!" and she laughed at the memory. I must say that Miriam was rather more sensibly dressed by the time we met her - no tweed skirts for her when riding her BSA in 1939.

"Ah yes, she was good company, but of course she was a little older than me and I've not heard from her for quite some time. She did some journalism for a bit and then I heard that she'd married a Mr. Lord, of Rex Motors I think it was."

She paused a little at this point and we waited for her - it really was all jolly interesting, as we'd only read about these people's goings on in the magazines and so meeting one of them in person was fascinating.

"Anyway, the Trial. Yes, well, we kept up a good pace along the Great North Road and, because of the dry weather, we didn't even have much problem with belt slip. We both had punctures of course, but we were carrying spare tyres and tubing so it didn't stop us. Edinburgh was much busier than we expected but we couldn't miss the Castle, so it was a quick turn-around, just stopping for refreshments and, well, y'know, easing, and then we were off again back down south. Muriel's young man was waiting for us again at about half way and he had refreshments ready for us. It was near Wetherby I seem to remember - but, oh! - it's amazing really after all these years, but I can clearly remember that he had chicken and ham, with glasses of white wine all set out and waiting for us. Fresh, warm gauntlets and scarves too. But it was swift - we had no time to spare and we were off again. I don't even have a memory of his face, just a 'thank-you' and we were back on the road." She paused and I reminded myself just what the Great North Road must have been like back then, but we call it the 'A1' now I suppose, what's left of it what with all the by-passes and 'improvements'... Anyway, back then it was almost completely un-tarred, just gravel and dust! It must have been a bit like riding in an ISDT. After all, they did call it a 'trial', didn't they!

"And then as soon as anything we were passing the Angel Islington once more and down through Aldergate back to Marble Arch. We did it in just twenty-two hours. There and back." She sighed at the memory.

"It was a long time ago - but it seems like only yesterday. And then, before we'd even had time to get home and relax, we got a letter from Muriel telling us of our next escapade! It seems she was keen to have a go at the John O' Groats to Land's End record next and that she thought that three tri-cars would be the best bet! Well, I didn't have a tri-car. I still don't and I don't want one. In the end, she did it on her own, but on her Rex motorcycle. All on her own as it turned out. And she did it! She broke the record. She was a sport, there's no doubt about it."

Just about that time we were passing through Frankfurt and I remember we could see lots of army vehicles on the roads, which didn't look too good, but then it was the first time I'd been in Germany so I didn't really know what to expect. Then there were all the red and black swastika flags flying from just about every public building and many more besides - we don't like to display much in the way of flags back here, do we? They did though, there were flags and banners everywhere.

The train stopped for some time at Frankfurt Central Station, or 'Frankfurt am Main' as it was labelled, and a young fellow came along the platform, rapping on the windows of the compartments and selling beers, ham rolls, cigarettes and things. I must say that this was all very welcome by that time. Of course, we hadn't a clue as to what he wanted for it, but thankfully Miriam had quite a few words of German. She went to the door in the corridor and sorted it all out for us, which involved a bit of arguing and finally handing over some Reichsmark coins, whereupon he muttered 'Heil Hitler' and dashed off. That seemed fair enough to us - until she came back in and explained to us just what the drinks, food and ciggies had actually cost us! Anyway, we settled up with her and vowed not to be cheated again. But we were, of course.

Then we were off, slowing through Offenbach and then stopping while a huge convoy of tanks crossed the line, but then off again and back up to speed. Miriam was looking out of the window and dozing while the others were fast asleep, so just Lavinda and I got to talking.

"So your rider, it's Graham Oates isn't it? He's delayed you say. But why? What happened? Will he make it?" Of course, I didn't know if he'd make it, but I could partially explain why he was late.

"Do you know Graham, then?" I asked.

"Oh no, not at all. I mean, I know about him of course and I've even been into his motorcycle shop in Liverpool, in Walton isn't it? So perhaps I met him there, but, hmm - we haven't been formally introduced" she said, putting on a jokingly posh tone of voice.

"Well, you'll like him. Quietly spoken, tall, dark hair and with a small moustache. Oh, and he can only see with one eye, not that it seems to bother or slow him down at all. He once told me he'd lost it as a result of being gassed in the trenches - well, near the trenches, as he was a dispatch rider, unsurprisingly. It got him away from the Front though, and back to the Island."

"The island?"

"Oh, THE island - the Isle of Man. That's where he was born, and still lived until well after the Great War, when he wasn't riding around Britain or Canada of course. Then he went over to Liverpool to work for Ebbs, in Walton, before he ended up buying the whole shop."

It's surprising how much you pick up about a bloke when you're working together in a small workshop for a few nights - and did he have some tales to tell! Long, long rides, all on his own in the middle of nowhere, he wasn't scared, he just did it. He really was an amazing chap you know, but then we got on well together - and I did respect him. A real British Bulldog if ever there was one! Oh, maybe I was overegging it a bit, but I suppose I was rather proud of being his partner in the Inter of all things.

Lavinda grinned at my enthusiasm.

"Well, I'm looking forward to meeting him then - and he's done a lot of trials riding too, hasn't he. Solo though, not outfits?"

"Both! Mostly solos though - he's been doing one-day trials for years on his Red Hunter, but then Ariels have always looked after him - after all, he did them a lot of good with his well publicised Canada trips. What's more, he's now their main dealer for Liverpool too. Then he got a Gold in the 1933 ISDT, riding a Square-Four outfit, which must have been really good advertising for their new cammy six-hundred. So yes, he's done a bit. Oh, and then he rode a big Squariel outfit in the Inter last year too. But that wasn't so good - he lost a few marks on the first day, and then the chair let him down on the Tuesday so he had to retire. It wasn't just him though - his pal, Harold Taylor, had exactly the same problem with his sidecar, but he managed to struggle on for a bit longer."

"Roddy and I have met Harold - and he's in the Ariel Team this year isn't he?"

"Yes, he was in their team last year too, in Wales. We're not though, we're in the South Liverpool Club team." I was enjoying talking with this attractive young lady - but just who was Roddy I wondered? "Harold's on another 1000cc Squariel outfit again this year, but then he always needs a sidecar, having just the one leg. As I said, just like Graham's, last year the bloody sidecar chassis cracked and he was out."

I don't deny it, I suppose I was enjoying showing off for her, y'know. But then I was young...

"It was a really tough one, the '38 was - in fact it was rather a bad year for weather all round, wasn't it. But we were there, just watching, and we saw Harold battling on. Y'know, out of the thirty five or so starters in that class, only about three finished - and only one got a Gold, managing no penalties at all. Tough it was." Lavinda was smiling again, I'm not sure why.

"Graham and you aren't in the works team though you say?"

"No, not this year, he's a private entrant riding for his Liverpool club. His shop's entered him I suppose. But he's supported by Ariels too of course. They're supplying the machine and Noxal are supplying the chair. Let's hope it's a bit stronger than last year's, whatever that was. But this one's got suspension on the sidecar wheel, so I'll be in the lap of luxury, won't I?"

"And the lap of honour too, I'm sure!" She looked lovely when she smiled.

"Oh yes, I'm sure! We'll see. Mind you, he's lucky to have it at all. Ariels promised him the machine some time ago, so long as it'll be run as an outfit, and he agreed, but since then I'm afraid they've delayed and delayed. He told me that he'd been down to Selly Oak recently, chasing up stock for his shop, but also pressing for the machine in time for the International. It seems that the factory is stepping up their production of military machines, supplying 350s and side-valve 500s for the Army - and even some for the French army too apparently. Anyway, they finally gave him a delivery date so he got an entry off to the A-CU just in time. Well, it was late, but they accepted it. So, last I heard he was still working hard preparing it. Our pal Arthur has been helping him line-up the sidecar and everything else, but the machine came with solo gearing, so they'll have had to change that too and I suppose that's why he's so late."

"So you'll be on a 1000? That's big. I mean, I know about the Broughs and Matchless vee-twins of course, but they've never been my cup of tea, y'know. I've always gone for the lighter ones, it's the 350s I like best."

"So what are you riding then - you are on a motorcycle, aren't you?" At that point I was aware that I may well have made a mistake that I'd really regret, but it was all right thank goodness.

"Oh yes, I'm on Felix, my new Ariel 350 Red Hunter. 'Felix IV' he's called really y'know. My first Felix was a 350 too and Roddy and I covered many happy miles on him. He was a delightful Dot-Bradshaw and seeing his lovely polished flywheel spinning around as we rode was wonderful.

Her cheerful smile at the thought of it briefly faded as she remembered something more. "Roddy would insist on calling it my 'Oil-Boiler' though, but then he was just jealous." This was all beginning to sound a bit silly to me, but I tried to join in.

"If you're going to call 'em names, I'm surprised you didn't call it 'Dorothy'. But why 'Felix'?" She didn't answer, thankfully ignoring my comment almost completely.

"Yes, he was a Dot - 'Devoid Of Trouble' - and it was true, he was well named. So I do miss Felix the First, but I'll have to admit that I appreciate the new Ariel's foot change..." She looked almost guilty at her infidelity, while I was almost embarrassed at her sillyness, but forgave her without her ever knowing.

"But then, none of my dear Felixes could hold a candle to the giant four-cylinder 1000cc monster that you'll be riding!"

"Hey - I'll not be riding it, y'know! I'll only be in the chair - but then it'll probably need all of its 997ccs to tow us along! Mind you, Graham's game for anything. He pedalled an 80cc autocycle round the National Rally last month!"

"Really? The National? But that's five or six hundred miles in 24 hours isn't it? No, come on - that's impossible on an autocycle!"

"No, really, it's true - and I did it with him. But we couldn't clock up the 600 miles! Oh no, we did manage about 350 miles though, but it was still hard work, I can tell you!"

"So, what were you on? I know nothing about these little tiddlers - although I'm not sure I really want to..." and she frowned, but it was quite clear that she was just winding me up.

Connor let out a giant snore at that point, and shifted onto his other side, but I ignored him. It could have been worse.

"Y'see, Graham's been selling autocycles as being an economical yet practical way of getting about and he saw the A-CU National Rally as being a good way to promote them. His main stock is the HEC Power Cycle, amongst others."

"Never heard of it." She was clearly becoming less impressed, so I tried harder.

"Oh it's a neat little machine - just 17 guineas on the road!"

"H.E.C.? What's that stand for then?"

52

"Er - Herbert? Er, no... ah! Hepburn Engineering Company, in London somewhere, but they moved up to Thorp Street in Birmingham just last year. That's behind the Hippodrome Theatre y'know, although I didn't know that when I went there to see 'Puss In Boots' as a kid! I think they moved because it uses an 80cc two-stroke engine made by Levis, at Stechford which isn't very far away."

"Levis! I had a Levis." It seemed that I'd managed to re-engage her enthusiasm with something she recognised "That was back in '24 I think and he was called 'Herbert', an unprepossessing little character who did me well for a bit. Herbert was a Model O, a 250 two-stoke, and a nice light little steed to ride he was too..." and Lavinda was briefly off elsewhere with the memory, while I was groaning at her naming her machines as if they were pets or servants or something, but she didn't notice, came back and carried on. "Although there's a lot of difference between an 80 and a full 250!" she pointed out.

"True," I admitted, although we really had done quite well just a couple of weeks ago and I wasn't going to play it down. "But it was quite a goer, and we had some fun going flat out most of the way, even if it was getting rather tiring towards the end. Mind you, not as bad as it was for Derek. Ha! Poor lad - he was on an HEC Racing Power Cycle." I still grin when I think of poor old Derek - he didn't want to be on the silly thing at all, but Graham had one in his showroom and since he'd got the idea in his head, Derek didn't have a lot of choice if he was to stay in employment!

"A racing autocycle? You're joking?"

"Well, I'm not joking, but maybe HEC were... Anyway, Graham had one in stock and he thought that, since for some unknown reason it hadn't sold, Derek could set the pace for us. Oh it looked the part alright - it had got narrow wheels, dropped handlebars, a Brooks B17 leather saddle and, er, that's about it really. Oh, and a rather special paint job. Oh yes, very flash it was - worth at least an extra half-a-mile an hour! But he couldn't stand the pace, poor lad. He dropped out after about twelve hours. Thanks to that narrow saddle probably. Graham gave him a ten-bob note to get back with and we carried on."

"Poor lad. And what were you riding? A supercharged one?"

"No no! Don't be silly. But since I quite like Scotts as you now know, I thought that one of the new Scott Cyc-Autos would raise the tone of the Team. For some reason Father was quite tickled by the whole thing, so he bought me one."

A sudden thought struck me. "Er - you must think that my father is very rich and has spoiled his boy, but in fact he's... Well, he's comfortably off as they say, but I never quite know what's coming next. Or not. Y'see, I'm not so much spoiled as randomly ruined I suppose, so when he remembers me, he's very generous, but most of the time I have to fend for myself. Anyway, the Cyc-Auto is a 98cc two-stroke, so it's got all of 18cc over the HEC - and it's got Scott front suspension too! So, telescopic forks, hub brakes, a clutch, twin exhausts - such luxury. Of course, that makes it rather heavier than the HEC, but we were well matched on the road."

"So come on - how did you do in the Rally?"

"Oh we did alright. We started in Liverpool of course - Graham's shop was one of the Rally Controls - and then we headed north, up through Preston, Lancaster, Kendal and then up to Carlisle. We had a rest and a bite to eat there, before swinging east and then south, because we were running short of time. We didn't make Hawick as we'd hoped. We'd both done it in previous years on bigger bangers, but we were really not covering the distance this time of course. Anyway, we still bagged 18 checkpoints and had covered, er.... 346 miles I think it was, by the time we got to the Final Control at Donington. And then I spread out on the grass and had a kip."

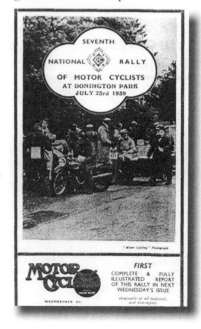

"Well, I'm not surprised! So, when was this, then? Last month did you say?" She was yawning as she said this, but still seemed quite interested.

"Yes, July 22nd and 23rd. And a lovely day on Sunday it was too, bright sunshine. Oh, and when we got to the circuit at Donnington Park, the field full of machines was a sight to see - they said that there were nearly 900 entries! In some ways, it was a sort of warm-up for this week as there were so many keen riders, with army, police, RAC and CSMA teams and even a few of them on German and Italian machines, although not many. Almost all British stuff really, but all sorts with two and three wheelers together. Lots of Morgans of course, but I saw a couple of BSAs too and somebody was even doing it in a Raleigh three-wheeler delivery van would you believe!"

The **RALEIGH**
LIGHT DELIVERY VAN

PRICE
75GNS
AS WORKS
Or £15.15.0 deposit
and 18 months
payments of £3.19.10
(About G.P. terms include
full interest)

LOAD up to 5 cwts.

Only two weeks after the event it was still fresh in my memory, tired though I had been at the time after the long ride - but then I looked up and saw Lavinda really was sleepy, sitting in the steadily jogging railway carriage listening to me rabbiting on and her eyelids were dropping a bit, so I thought I'd just finish my tale off and then we'd have a kip perhaps.

"Y'know, even after that long ride Graham didn't ever really seem tired and he was still keen to wander round looking at the machines in the parking area. Then he got hold of one of the National Rally Programmes for the spectators and came rushing back to wake me up and show me the quote in it from Sir Malcolm Campbell: *'The new Ariel Square Four is without doubt a very great credit to the British Motorcycle Industry.'*"

"'That's what we'll be riding in Germany, m'boy!' he said, slapping me on the shoulder. 'You mark my words, we'll show the Krauts a thing or two!' Well, that was really was a bit rude, eh?" and I grinned, looking over to Lavinda again - only to see that she'd finally drifted off and was hard fast asleep.

I'd been talking to myself.

The pushrod 600cc Ariel 4F had been launched in 1937, along with the 1000cc version, the 4G.
In Ariel nomenclature, G denoted the touring models, while H denoted the sports models.
The lesser known 1000cc 4H was introduced in 1939 with cycle parts much like the 4F as seen above,
having 20" front and 19" rear wheels, narrow mudguards and a smaller tank than the 4G,
but with siamesed exhaust pipes.
However, neither the 4F nor the 4H were reintroduced after the war.
In total, 536 of the 4F model and only 151 of the 4H model were ever made.
Only three genuine 4H machines are currently known to have survived.

CHAPTER 5

- in which they experience a bit of Culture

"YOU MEAN you were all sleeping in the carriage? What about your bunks, or sleeping compartments?" Andy had been across Europe in his gap year before university, but even then he hadn't had to sleep rough, so he is a little surprised by the image his grandfather is describing. However, Eric puts him straight about how rough tough motorcyclists used to live and then he gets on with his story.

Tuesday 15th August, 1939

We finally arrived in Salzburg, and a real to-do it was, I can tell you. Do you know, they weren't really expecting us! They thought we'd all back off, given the, now what did they call it back in the early days? - 'political tension' - yes, tension - until Hitler stretched it too far and it snapped that is!

So they weren't ready for us. Oh, they'd got the entries in from the A-CU, but then as they hadn't heard much since then they assumed we'd not turn up. A right game it was, what with hurriedly sorting out the hotels for us, garaging for the bikes and all, but they did finally get us all sorted out with enough rooms to stay. Very well organised they were really - although we did have to stay in a Gasthof some way out of town. Mind you, it could have been worse, as poor old Colin Edge had to borrow a bicycle to ride the one and a half miles or so from his Gasthaus to the Start each day!

We'd all arrived about a week early for practice - and then they told us that we were all invited to the Annual Salzburg Music Festival. Well, that wasn't really what we'd gone there for, but then why not? As usual it seemed, it was to run from the beginning of August through to September, so they'd be well out-running our mere six days. Some of us went along in the evenings after we had spent the day looking around the place, playing tourists, while the riders had been out almost all day getting used to the local roads, riding on the right, figuring out what the road signs meant and checking their machines were all tickety-boo.

I was just kicking my heels of course, feeling a bit at a loose end while I waited for Graham, although Salzburg was indeed a lovely city and by the Friday I had seen quite a bit of it. The cathedral, or the Salzburger Dom as they call it, was lovely, especially the giant dome in the middle. Now that was really something! - and old - oh it was old - we were told that the church had been built on the site of a Roman town, way back in the 8th Century!

It was all very interesting and relaxing, only feeling a bit odd when every shop assistant, tram conductor and barman seemed to have start with the Nazi salute and finish with "Heil Hitler". I didn't respond to it, but others did in various ways, presumably feeling that they had to – or maybe just taking the piss. I don't know, I just kept out of it.

Now, I'm not really one for big orchestral stuff, but the Festival looked really very impressive and some of the others were quite excited by it all. It was held all over the town, in the Grosse Festspielhaus - the 'Grand Festival Hall'; the Haus für Mozart - the 'House for Mozart' and the Felsenreitschule. This last one made us laugh when we found out that it just translated to the 'Cliffside Riding Academy'! Oh, and we went to one in the Domplatz too, but I suppose it was the Festival Hall that was most impressive.

It had been redecorated earlier that year and they were keen to tell us that they had replaced all the old wood panelling with a gold decorated, plaster ceiling. They should have left it as it was in my opinion.

They told us all about the Festival, followed by the Inter's Opening Ceremony and that we would be greeted by Der Führer himself.

Well, that never happened, I don't know why.

Miriam was particularly excited about it all though - she'd heard all about it before we got there and was disappointed to have missed some of it. Nevertheless, she enjoyed telling us all about the wonderful Vienna Philharmonic Orchestra, although it seemed that it had recently been reorganised a bit, with all the Jewish musicians being replaced by Aryans. Miriam thought it wouldn't matter though.

I wouldn't know, I preferred Big Band music in those days. In fact I really used to like Billy Cotton's Band - but then he wasn't just a band leader y'know, oh no. He was a pilot in the Great War and then a racing driver too! I even met him once - but that was a different story I suppose.

Salzburg

Behind the scenes, the new regime had deemed the entrance foyer of Der Grosse Festspielhaus, with Anton Faistauer's classic frescoes, to be 'gloomy and out of date' and entrusted Reich Set-Designer Benno von Arent to completely redesign the rooms ready for the 1939 Festival, at which a number of Nazi celebrities were to appear.

They arrived punctually for the opening ceremonies in a train of open-topped Mercedes cars, with Hermann Göring, in a white uniform bedecked with medals and standing up in the back giving the Nazi salute. He was followed by Propaganda Minister Joseph Goebbels and Heinrich Himmler, the Reichsführer of the SchutzStaffel, the SS. They attended the performance of 'Der Rosenkavalier', whereupon a bust of Goebbels was erected in the Entrance Hall. Austria's new Governor, Baldur von Schirach, gave a 'suitable speech', culminating with "In Mozart's name, we call the young to arms". Adolf Hitler made an appearance at two Mozart operas, the first being 'Don Giovanni' on 9 August. A few days later, on 14 August when they had just arrived in Salzburg, Godber-Ford and a few others of the British contingent saw Hitler arrive for 'Die Entführung aus dem Serail'. Godber-Ford later recalled that Hitler was in a blue suit, looking smaller than he expected, and flanked by Martin Bormann and Albert Speer.

What the British may not have noticed however was the difference in atmosphere at the festival compared to previous years. There was a surprisingly lax dress code, while seemingly large numbers of 'imported' Bavarian beer drinkers made it clear that elegance was no longer of the greatest importance, while a 'good turn out' was essential.

As well as many of the usual festival attendees being missing, there were others who were particularly noticeable by their absence. Toscanini had refused to perform in protest to the Anschluss - the 'union' of Germany and Austria - the previous March. Both Bruno Walter and Vladimir Horowitz had gone to the USA, as had members of orchestras and other artists, and so the VPO looked very different with all the familiar Jewish faces missing.

The programme was mainly Germanic, being comprised almost entirely of the works of Beethoven, Richard Strauss, Mozart, Wagner and Brahms. Notable amongst those who did appear were Helge Rozvaenge, the Danish operatic tenor, who performed 'The Magic Flute', and Friedrich Wührer, the left-handed pianist, who performed Schmidt's 'Quintet' - but using both hands that day.

Plans were changed quite often, at least on two occasions thanks to Hitler's intervention. It seems that he'd had a disagreement with Mussolini and retired to nearby Berchtesgaden, so missing both the rest of the festival and the start of the ISDT. Then, despite the festival being planned to run from the 1st August to the 8th September as was usual, part of the way through it was unexpectedly announced that the Festival would terminate on the 31st, ostensibly because the VPO was needed to perform 'Die Meistersinger' at a Nazi Party Convention in Nuremberg. Of course it later became apparent that the true reason was that the German army was going to invade Poland on the 1st September.

CHAPTER 6
- in which Eric's team-mate finally arrives

"Hey! Graham! Where have you been?" I'd heard the distinct note of a Squariel at about midday that Friday and turned to see Graham Oates swinging into the hotel car-park. He had already lifted his goggles, presumably to ask where to go and where he was being billeted, and his face really was a sight! Two round, white discs encircled his eyes, while the rest of his face was caked with dust - you couldn't even see his 'tash. Mind you, we were all looking much like that by the end of the first day of the trial!

"Where have I been? I've been inspecting these big new straight roads they've been busy building all over the place. I must admit that you can keep up a fair pace on them, although that concrete's knocked hell out of my tyres. I hope the Dunlop boys are here!"

"Yes, they're here. But hey, we were worried about you Graham. You've left it 'til the last minute, haven't you! What delayed you?"

"Lots of things, oh lots... When the bike finally turned up we had to get the gearing right and the sidecar lined up correctly - but they'd sent the wrong fittings - and it's still not right - my shoulder's killing me! As always, the fettling took much longer than we expected. Look, I'll tell you all about it all later, but right now, is there any chance of a nice cold beer?" We sorted him out and watered him, then we heard the rest of his story later on.

It seemed that he'd been so late setting off that it had been a mad dash to get over to Salzburg in time and it was only with the assistance of a letter from the FICM that he'd cleared the customs into Germany quickly enough. Then he'd really hammered east along the Autobahns with the big Ariel running hot and fast, but going well all the way. It looked like he'd only just made it though.

However, there was still the preparation of the outfit to be done - and, like Marjorie, he'd run in the engine on the way over! That meant I had to drain the tank and sump and do a full oil change. I checked the gearbox and chaincase too while I was at it - but it was all in good order with no signs of any metal at all in the sump filter.

We got a new set of tyres from the trade van - Dunlop Universals they were - and I took the opportunity to stow a couple more spare tubes away in the chair. It really was very hot that summer, over 90 degrees or so, and changing the three tyres was warm work, so I pulled my shirt off and got on with it. Whereupon one of the 'uniforms' immediately came across the paddock waving his bayonet around and insisting that I put it back on again! Well, it wasn't worth the fuss and I suppose it was all their country by then, so I put it back on – only feeling slightly cheered by the fact that he looked a lot hotter in his thick, high collared uniform than me!

Graham had already done the usual trials preparation and had spare cables taped to the forks and chainstays, with spare spokes, bulbs, sparking plugs and a CO_2 bottle for rapid tyre inflation all packed away in the sidecar.

He'd done it all before of course, so everything was in place - and having the sidecar meant that we could carry a good tool kit as well – we even had extra long tyre levers, so that was a bonus. We were certainly better off than the solo riders, who strapped their tools on where they could.

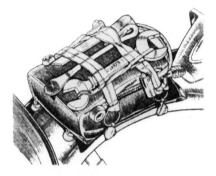

I checked all the cables, chains and clearances, but there were only the chains and one exhaust tappet needing adjusting and so apart from that it was just about ready to go. After all, it was a new machine, fresh from the factory - and they knew what he was going to do with it so we assumed that they'd taken particular care preparing it for him. But then, little were we to know!

I was a bit disappointed to find that Graham's sidecar was just the same model as was fitted to both Harold Taylor's and Bill Peacock's Squariels. Interestingly, Ernie Smith, the Ariel Team Manager, and Bob Holliday were on a Squariel outfit too, but their chair was an old one and a lot slimmer and lighter.

Oh, certainly I was nice and comfortable in the Noxal, with it being quite large and with a sprung wheel as well, but it was rather cumbersome - not like a real trials chair at all really - so we needed all of the 1000cc to haul the beast around on the rough. Graham wasn't impressed either, getting me to both increase the toe-in and give it lean-in for riding on the right.

Noxal sidecar fitted to the Ariel Square Four

Despite the improvements, Graham was still grumbling throughout that it wasn't a patch on the sleek, nimble outfit he'd ridden back in '33, the one with with the cammy 600 engine.

Anyway, we took it out for a test-run later that afternoon - and I'd not actually ridden with Graham before. I'd already done a fair bit of sidecarring though and Graham didn't really need a passenger anyway, so we got on well right from the start. Mind you, I found his full-on 'wide throttle whenever possible' technique initially took some getting used to, but I soon got to trust him and was looking forward to really getting into it on the Monday. We headed out across country.

What really surprised us was to see so many women working in the fields that evening and, it being harvest time, cutting the corn with scythes – almost no men and no machines. There were women working on the roads too and this wasn't quite what we expected to see in 'modern Germany', but that's how it was.

We only got lost once - we were just swanning about to check out both us and the outfit really - but there was always someone happy to help. We soon realised that there was an usually large number of impressively smart black uniforms of one sort or another around. They were directing the traffic, marshalling everything and everybody and guarding just about every doorway for some reason, so it was looking more like an army exercise than a trial - but that's just the way they did it then I suppose.

On Saturday there were all the entry and team registrations to be done and the NSKK chappies (NationalSozialistisches KraftfahrKorps, the German Motor Corps), were very efficient with everything prepared, all done in triplicate and carbon-copies all over the place. Then we had the weighing-in, with all the spots of bother usually associated with that game, then our competition numbers handed out, rules explained - and the Germans had plenty of rules I can tell you, dead keen on them they were - and then the teams were allocated places on the parc-fermé.

The Press were there too, and I spotted Arthur Bourne from the Blue 'Un making notes, with a photographer alongside - I didn't know him of course, but recognised him from pictures. It was funny to see how different our blokes were compared to the German and Italian press, who were constantly lining their competitors up for formal shots, while the chap from the Green 'Un, the writer called 'Cyclops', was getting snaps of just as it was in the parc-fermé and round about. I later found he was Peter Chamberlain, who was also representing the A-CU at the event.

It took all day, with lots of waiting around out in the sun and it was a really hot summer that year, have I mentioned that? However, the other thing the Germans were good at was making lots of cold, thin beer available, so it could have been worse. I'd already met up with Gustav, who was Dick's friend really, and he introduced me to Otto, who knew where to find the beer. Then Graham came back over with a wry grin on his face.

"Now look what they've given us! We've not even started yet, and already I've got a gong!" He'd got a lovely bronze medal, sitting in dark blue velvet lined box, celebrating that year's ISDT - I had a closer look.

"Gosh, that's rather nice. Where's mine then?"

"Oh no, they're only for the riders - you're just ballast! It's bloody ridiculous anyway, but let's hope that's the end to all the pomp and circumstance - I just want to get on with it!" But no, there was lots to come before that...

Graham Oates' own 1939 ISDT Starter's Medal

Then on the Sunday they made the official start to it all, with all their fancy parades, marching up and down before the Opening Ceremony. It was held in Franz-Joseph Park in Salzburg and there was first to be a parade of the teams in the square in the afternoon. As it turned out it wasn't all the teams parading, oh no, not us, it was mostly just the army and police. Their boss in charge of the whole event was Korpsführer General Adolf Hühnlein, head of the NSKK, and he took the parades, with lots of marching, stamping and saluting going on for nearly an hour! I'll never forget it, us standing in the background watching it all - competitors but just spectating.

The French army teams came in first, dressed in the most elaborate blue coats, red britches and what have you, all very theatrical. Oh, they looked very attractive, although their Gendarme Team was all in black. They all marched along in line to the strains of the 'Marseillaise' of course. Mind you, I've no idea why they were there because in the event I didn't see any French riders competing at all...

The Dutch came on next, but there were not many of them and they didn't make a fuss, just marched on through.

The Italians followed them and they were all in immaculate white uniforms, mostly air force. White! - well I ask you, was that practical? And I'll never forget those trousers - they were so stiffly starched that it looked as if sitting down would've cracked them! However, when they marched in the people cheered loudly, so it must have appealed to some. Marjorie was standing next to me at that point and had to stifle her laughter.

The Germans marched in to the 'Deutschlandlied', their national anthem, with the brass band busting their buttons to get the maximum volume out of their instruments. There were lots of them, every one of them in uniform, even the NSKK support crews, but they didn't look so good to our eyes. Their posh riding breeches weren't our idea of breeks and their boots made no sense at all: they were very smart, very high and very shiny, but they didn't look comfortable! Oh, they all looked extremely efficient, but rather dour as they marched on. Probably their boots were hurting.

The three British army teams were there in uniform too of course, a thin khaki line, but after already seeing all those parade ground perfectionists Marjorie turned and whispered in my ear: "My hat, what are our lads going to look like?" You see, they'd already ridden all the way over to Germany and then been riding around the countryside to acclimatise and familiarise themselves, and so she was right - by that time some of them could have looked a little worse for wear.

What made it worse was that they'd brought no dress uniforms for an official occasion - they'd only got their battledress and riding gear and so I sadly tended to agreed with her. "Hmmm, I'm afraid you're right Marjie, they're probably going to look pretty ropey compared to those lot..."

But no, as it turned out they were all right - being mostly guards officers, they had their secret weapon up their sleeves, or below their trousers; top quality boots made in England! So, even though by then they were pretty worn, they were highly polished. Oh yes, real British Army, all spit & polish for the occasion - although their crews were still just in fatigues. They marched on like one man and they were magnificent. The crowd were mostly Austrians, but there were a surprising number of British there to watch as well, and they really cheered them on! We were so proud because, as I say, they could have looked such a crumby lot...

By something of a contrast, the rest of us, the British riders, works and club teams, private entries, crews and supporters, we could be spotted from way off beneath a cloud of tobacco smoke - we were relaxed after having been doing all that prep and riding, so we were mostly in our dirty grey flannels and open neck shirts – but then we weren't in the army.

And then the speeches began. Korpsführer Hühnlein was up on stage again with a public address system welcoming us all to "The Olympiad of Motorsports", which made it all sound very grand. He went on about "...sportsmanship, friendship between nations, motor-sport comrades..." and lots more that I can't remember now. Then another brass-hat got up and told us that there should "...always be competition between the military sides of nations..." but he didn't exactly explain why.

I suppose it all took a long time because the speeches were being translated into Italian by the boss of the Itie teams and into English for us by Joe Woodhouse.

Some of Hühnlein's cracks made us laugh, although the others didn't seem to see the jokes for some reason - no sense of humour some of them. We agreed about the friendship bit - most of our riders had been pleased to meet old friends from Italy, Germany, Holland and all - they were people they'd met while riding in Wales, or wherever the events had taken place in previous years. So when Hühnlein finally finished - and he did go on rather a long time - and Joe had given us the gist of it, we gave him a bit of a clap, only to find that wasn't what was expected and they frowned at us! Oh well, it was all meant in good spirits.

Now, quite why they had to do it on top of everything else I don't know, but the troops then had to be inspected. So there they were, all lined up at attention in the hot sun, while a bunch of officers wandered up and down inspecting. We felt sorry for them but didn't wait to watch - we went for a beer.

That evening was the Governor's Reception and Major Watling, the Steward for the whole British entry, together with Peter Bradley, Peter Chamberlain and Miss Bunce from the A-CU, Colonel Bennett and the army officers, all went for drinks, tiny sandwiches, polite small talk and more speeches. There was no invitation to any of the teams or private entries, and certainly not for the crews, but I didn't miss it at all because by then we were comfortably settled down in one of Salzburg's cosy Bierkellers with some of the German and Dutch chaps.

The Official Programme, as given to all competitors and spectators

Korpsführer General Adolf Hühnlein, NSKK
Being at the head of the Motor Corps, he'd had overall responsibility for
the introduction of the Autobahns and organising the German Grand Prix.
The 1939 ISDT was the last motoring event
with which he was to be involved before the war started.
He died in 1942

CHAPTER 7

ANDY IS LOOKING a little puzzled.

"But, can you really speak German then Granddad? I didn't know! Like, you've often mentioned talking to them, and now you say you spent the rest of the afternoon and all evening drinking with them, and with the Dutch guys too come to that - how did you get on?"

"Well..." and Eric hesitates for moment. "It was a long time ago and I haven't used it much since. Your grandma and I did go to France a few times y'know, but not back to Germany, so I never had the opportunity to practice it much..." Andy is still waiting, so Eric tries a little harder.

"But I do still have a few useful German words y'know. '*Fünf Biere bitte*', and that means..." but Andy cut him short.

"Oh, c'mon, I know what that means, and like I thought – Sie können Deutsches nicht sprechen, so how <u>did</u> you get on with your pals? I don't think that they all spoke good English like most of them do nowadays – did they?"

"We got on - we had a lot in common y'know and lots of words make sense wherever you come from, with a little help and waving our hands about, y'know how it is. Some of those chaps had pretty good English I'll have to admit, they all learned it in school so they told me, both the Germans and the Dutch. We only had French and Latin in school when I was a boy and neither was any good at all to us there. But after a bit, as the night went on, the beer helped too!" and they both laugh at the thought of it. "Come to think of it, isn't it time for a beer, don't you think lad?"

"Gramps! It's early afternoon and the sun isn't even approaching the yard-arm yet. I'll make another cuppa tea in a while, but don't give up on your story - when did the Trial actually get round to starting?"

"Monday. That's when the Inters start. Very early on the Monday morning..."

TRAJECT

van de
INTERNATIONALE
ZESDAAGSCHE

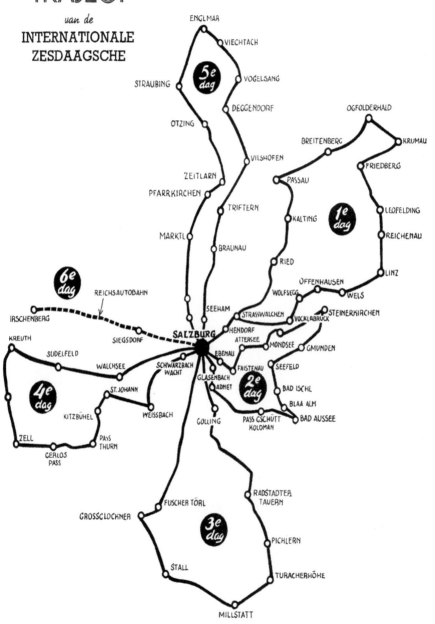

We were all up for the Start at five in the morning, out on the edge of Salzburg. It was going to be good weather - already clear, with the mountains showing sharply in the distance. It was all very exciting, for me at least, and probably for most of the 267 starters lined up and rarin' to go. Silly really, as Graham and I weren't starting for another hour or so, but we just had to be there for the first day's start!

We had already been given the plan of action – the map of the six days' routes, or the *'Traject'* as they called it. Graham called it our 'trajectory'.

Mind you, they weren't all there at the Start that morning. When we looked at the Starters List, posted up at the Kontrol in the flag-infested paddock, we could see that there were eleven non-starters, all of them German. That caused us some amusement – had they bottled out at the last minute? Probably not, but then why had the whole of their Vase 'B' Team retired? The Germans gave no explanation at all, but we sort of knew that something was happening over east in Poland, so maybe the three Zundapp outfits had suddenly been posted away? Maybe their machines were being repainted in 'Wehrmacht Field-Grau' and it hadn't dried yet? Malcolm was joking of course, but perhaps he had unknowingly been sort of right after all? Anyway, the outfits had been replaced at the last minute by three solos, but the other eight, the two listed BMWs, four NSUs, the TWN and the Triumph - the German Triumph and nothing to do with our Triumphs of course - they were all out of it for some reason.

I must say that the big bang when they set off the maroon at exactly 5am did make me jump. It startled Major Watling too, who was then a bit late in raising his flag, but the big cheer that then went up as the first riders set off was almost as loud! I'd seen nothing like this the previous year in Llandrindod Wells, but then that's not the way we did it, was it? Anyway, we don't know to what degree the locals had been put up to it - maybe they had been 'volunteered'? Certainly there always seemed to be plenty of supporters all over the place for the German riders, all seemingly well organised and waving lots of flags.

Nevertheless, I felt quite proud to get a good cheer when we eventually set off. There were sixty or so of us competing that year, but I hadn't known that there were quite so many British spectators there as well!

As we had learned early on, the German way of doing it was to have uniformed SS men all over, controlling the traffic and the flag-waving crowds and just being seen to be there. They did a good job though – it all went very smoothly. Well controlled.

Anyway, we were off at last and Graham was in good form with the outfit going well too – we'd fixed the handling and it steered neutrally at about 30mph, and steady above that as long as the damper was well screwed down, so that was fine. Not that Graham spent much time at a mere 30. Oh no, he pushed on right from the start.

Day One headed out north-east from Salzburg into the Sudeten area of Czechoslovakia, which I suppose they felt they could do as they'd recently taken the place over!

Of course, this was all terra incognita for us, and probably for almost all the other riders too, but it was very well marked all along the way and we had no problems in that respect. The promising start to the day's weather held true and it was excellent – very warm, dry and clear. Although we'd been rather chilly standing around in our thin jackets at the Start so very early in the morning, we soon warmed up and were far too busy to think about it 'til mid afternoon when we stopped at a Kontrolle and I took the opportunity to unzip my jacket.

As we rode out of the city and through Hendorf and to Strasswalchen where the first time-control was, we were getting onto increasingly second-class roads, quite broken in places. It didn't bother Graham though – he just zig-zagged through the worst of it, hardly slowing at all. However, although we'd greatly improved the outfit's handling, it was still a big lump. Oh, it looked like a trials chair alright, but it was heavy – it was all that suspension I suppose. Obviously they'd had to improve on the ones that had broken the previous year, but quite why they'd then lumbered us with those overweight sidecars I'll never know – unless it was a background business deal between Ariels and Noxal? If so, I wish those concerned had been made to drive one themselves across Sudetenland that week! Sadly the strain soon began to show, what with all that rough terrain and the need for lots of steering damper too – after all, Graham had only had a day or so's rest after riding all the way across from Birmingham.

Nevertheless, it was all great fun! Graham's strategy was to make as good time as we could in case of delays or problems. Y'see, that first day, after the Start there were eleven Zeitkontrollen, that's time-control posts, all along the route before the final one at the Finish and there were penalties if you arrived early or left late. The trick was to get there as quickly as possible and if we were early, we'd have a brief rest and check things over within sight of the Kontrolle - and then get there spot on time. In fact it turned out that some of the chaps on duty didn't mind if you turned up a little early and did a little bit of tweaking there, but others stuck exactly to the rules, so it wasn't worth risking it.

So we were making good progress and even got past a couple of DKW solos, until we found ourselves behind an NSU outfit, number 154. By the way, our number was 39, but they hadn't sent us off in numerical order. We later found out it was Faron Walther and his crew Jens in the German outfit and by jove did they motor. I mean, well, they'd only got 600cc to our 1000, but they didn't hang about! Clearly Graham was trying to get past, but we couldn't, no matter how hard he tried. They were good!

Until they slowed, pulled over to the right, and then stopped. We slowed too and Graham shouted at them.

"All right?" If it was just their bike, then tough luck – but if one of them was hurt that would be different of course.

73

"Nein – der Motor ist krank…" He was clearly not happy. We were though – and with a wave and "Good luck!" we were off again.

We met Faron later in the hotel and he told us about it. Apparently, the NSU engine was the new 601 OSL - a 562cc OHV single designed by Walter Moore, who had defected to NSU from Norton - so they were busy making ersatz Norton Cammies in Germany! What a nerve. However, it had only come out late in '38 and hadn't really had a lot of development, probably because NSU, like most of the German manufacturers, had been forced into production as fast as possible. So possibly not surprisingly, pushing the new bike very hard in the trial was testing it to the extreme – and the aluminium cylinder head's gasket blew, which is why it had run out of steam in front of us earlier that day. They had waited for it to cool, tightened the head down and got back, but with severe penalty points for time lost of course.

It seems that two of the three 601 OSLs in the NSU Team A, which was going for the Manufacturer's Team Trophy, had suffered the same way. However, Dunz, number 94, had previously got some inside information and had been tightening down his cylinder head each morning throughout Practice and so had got away with it.

"Dunz ist SS, aber Oettinger und I are NSKK, so he does not talk to us…" Some things were more important than the team, it seemed.

So we thundered on, while the roads became rougher and narrower until we approached Passau where it got a bit better for a stretch, but then out the other side and back onto rough roads before we arrived at the Breitenberg Kontrolle. We'd got all four timings right so far, still with no penalties, and so we pushed on into the mountains, brimming with confidence. However, it was there that things got interesting.

For a start, Austria had only recently gained the 'benefits' of becoming part of the German Republic and been converted to driving on the right. That's why most of the cars we saw in the towns were still right hand drive and we were quite amused to see 'Recht Fahren' (Keep Right) notices nailed to trees all over the place. It must have been a bit of an inconvenience for those wealthy enough to own a car as their the steering wheel would be on the right, but less so for solo motorcyclists – and for all the farmers with their horse and carts.

However, way out in the sticks, the local yokels had either not heard of the new rules, or had ignored them, so that Monday we were hurtling round a bend in the foothills only to come head to head with a bloody great wagon and horses on 'our' side of the road! Ambling along, its driver didn't seem to be at all worried – probably we were not the first to have to take sudden evasive action that morning and he was still undamaged, so he just carried on...

We shortly afterwards came across an Italian bike in the ditch, so presumably one of the yokels had scored at least once, but the rider gave us the thumbs up so we pushed on – watching ahead a little more carefully thereafter.

So despite the rural obstacle course, we were still doing well, but not everyone was as lucky. At Leonfelding Kontroll we met Graham Berry, one of the Army riders on his 500 Norton – but with rather modified controls. We had a couple of minutes in hand so, while he was busily working on the throttle cable and Graham was off for a piss, he told me that he'd been passing through one of the villages in the hills – there were quite a few that we'd all flown through, but with no Kontrolle located there they didn't really register – when a dog ran out in front of him! He hit it full on – and it was a big dog. Had him off of course and it bent the 'bars and buggered his twist-grip completely.

So when we saw him he'd already straightened the 'bars, bashed the front mudguard about back into shape and was arranging the throttle cable so he could operate the carb by pulling on the inner-cable with his thumb. That would have cramped his style a bit, especially over the rough, but he made it back to Salzburg alright and we saw him briefly in the parc fermé that night - but he didn't say how the dog got on.

75

In fact, parked next to him was Ernie Smith's WD 350 Matchless which was in a much worse state, with bent forks and a damaged front wheel. We didn't really get to hear what had happened until much later in the week when we were talking to Bert Perrigo, but apparently B.Q.M.S. Smith had also had an encounter with a local yokel on the wrong side of the road, only this time it wasn't a horse and cart, but a bus. Amazingly, Ernie was unhurt and had got back to base and had even bashed the bike's front end roughly back into shape, with the wheel only a few inches out of line. He'd gamely started on the Tuesday, but sadly had to retire before too long because of awful handling and a leaking petrol tank.

Anyway, there we were, pushing on up over the tops, still at maximum grongle and with seven Kontrollen satisfactorily under our belts and still with no penalty points, when suddenly the engine misfired. Graham lifted the petrol cap, peered in and refitted it, shaking his head as he reached down to the reserve tap.

The engine re-started, so it was fine – but we were high in the mountains, on reserve – and where was the next fuel stop? Presumably at the next Zeitkontrolle, but we didn't really know how far off that was… So from then on our pace lessened because he no longer used full throttle, then putting it into neutral and killing the engine on any downhill runs. We were well past the highest points and broaching the top of another long hill when it cut again. That was it. Nothing in reserve. So, just making it over the top, we coasted downhill for as far as we could.

God, it was frustrating to have rider after rider sweeping past us! But what could we do? Pedal? And do you know, no-one stopped to offer us a drop of their petrol. But then, it was a bit more of a competitive event I suppose, not like the MCC jollies that we'd both done before down in the West Country.

We had to get off and push it when we rolled to a stop just before the crest of a small hill, but then got going again down the other side when we saw in the distance the big red and black banner of Dornach Kontrolle on our side of the town. We quietly free-wheeled in and so they knew exactly what we wanted, waving Graham on to the petrol pumps just beyond, while I leaped out with our Kontrolkarte.

Oh, we got lots of penalties for that, so we'd messed our clean sheet after all, but we were soon back in action with a full tank again. Graham told me that we really should be carrying a spare can of petrol, so presumably it was all my fault, but then I suppose that was all part of my job as passenger, TSR, whipping boy, whatever necessary really...

However, being late for that Kontrolle was bad enough, but if we didn't make up our lost time, we'd gain yet more penalties at the next one! So, in his usual style, Graham twisted the grip.

And gosh, did we fly!

By that time the day had become really quite warm, and sitting right next to that big iron four cylinder block busily buzzing away by my right shoulder was like being hunched up with a brazier in a foundry and a turbine at maximum revs as close company. I'm sure my right ear has never been the same since. That bike really went though. I mean, despite having a bloody great rowing boat bolted to it, the Squariel still went as fast as my Scott, bowling along at up to 80 or so on the good bits of road.

The trouble was that other bits of the road weren't good, they were really rough, but by that time Graham wasn't prepared to ease off and he just hammered the outfit over even the roughest bits. Something just had to give and eventually it was the rear wheel spindle. Mind you, it was under dire circumstances and I'll never criticise the Ariel for that one.

It happened like this. We were tearing along and heading into a long gentle left-hander when suddenly we saw a bike in the road – a small green DKW it was I think, but who cares, it was the rider that worried us. A black figure was down on the road ahead of us and all Graham could do was to shut off and yank the bars, violently swerving to the left – we were going far too fast and it was too close for us to stand any chance of stopping. Inevitably the sidecar's wheel lifted – nothing I could do in time – and then we swerved back to the right, slamming the chair's wheel back down. Thankfully that meant that we missed the fallen rider – rode neatly round, back on almost two wheels again – and went off the road, over the ditch - and then over the hedge! Right over the top! As I said, we had been going quickly.

We landed in the field and the ground was rock-hard so it was a hell of a crash when we hit – but we kept moving. It's sometimes a lot worse when you look back at it, but at the time you just get on with it and we rode on, through a gate and out of the field and back down the road as if that was just the usual way it was done!

Leaping off, we ran to see if the rider was alright – well Graham did, while I went further back up the road to warn any oncoming riders. In fact there was no more traffic for a time and the DKW rider was unhurt, if a little shaken. She even managed to help Graham drag her bike off the road and when I returned she was thanking us and waving us on. So, fairly sure that she really was alright, we climbed aboard, re-started, waved and rolled off. Only to find, now that we were paying a bit more attention, that the back-end wasn't behaving at all like it should. We stopped and investigated. The rear wheel spindle had pulled out of the offside fork-end.

Tool-kit out, loosened the spindle nuts – and found that the nearside fork-end had bent slightly. Well, it's amazing what you can do with the big rocks that are often conveniently provided by the roadside.

We pushed on along some pretty rough roads, and even across a ford, although the recent dry weather meant that it wasn't as challenging as the organisers probably intended! Anyway, the back axle stood up to it and we had no more problems.

78

I'm afraid to have to admit that we were still going a bit too fast for those un-mettaled roads and we slid on the gravel a few times and then particularly badly on a tight right-hander, bouncing off the road - and not just the once either - but always swinging back onto the road again.

I suppose Graham was getting tired, across his shoulders for sure, but you really wouldn't know as he wasn't giving up at all, stretching the throttle cable at every opportunity. By then I'll admit that I was beginning to wish he would ease up a bit, but no, he pushed on, trying to make up time.

We were heading for Wels next and swept down into a pine forest leading down into the Linz valley. It must have been the particularly hot weather, but there were a lot of pine needles in the road and in places they had gathered in quite thick carpets. We hit one of them half way round a fast left-hand curve. I was hanging well out of the chair of course and we were really in complete control – by then we were forming into a well synchronised team of two and could really get round the bends fast. But not over a bed of slippery pine needles.

We didn't tip, but just slid gracefully sideways into the forest. I got back into the chair in a hurry, not knowing what was coming next. It turned out to be a pair of giant pines patiently waiting for us, but which were placed just too close together for us to get through and we came to a rather sudden halt.

"*Bloody hell!* Don't just sit there – help me pull us out and get going!" Graham was a bit cross and I was the only one around to shout at... But to be fair, I suppose I was a bit shaken and was indeed still sitting in the chair, but I pulled myself together, jumped out and we heaved at the back of the outfit to un-jam it from between the two trees. However, it was too well stuck. After all, it had hit the gap dead-centre at, what, about 20mph I suppose? Stuck right in it was, like a cork in a bottle.

A few miles back we had swept past a chap on a solo BMW and he came along just then. To our surprise – and delight – he stopped and, without a word spoken, joined our heaving party. The extra pull worked and we were free. We thanked him of course but he was away, back off to his bike which he'd left still ticking over on the road. Thankfully our outfit didn't seem to have suffered too much from its unconventional method of stopping, although the chair's nose was a bit dented.

So off we went again, with Graham only slightly moderating our pace through a ford. It was amazing really. After four fairly violent incidents in a short time, we were still all in good order and bowling along pretty quickly really. Oh, not quite as quickly as we had set out, admittedly, but not touring for sure. We were then on the last leg of Day One.

We got through Wels Kontrolle, late of course, and then through Offenhausen and to Ungenach Kontrolle, finding we'd made up a little time, but not enough. Hurtling through Wolfsegg and laughing at the name, we were heading for Vocklamarkt Kontrolle, which was the last one before the end, so our chances of catching up our lost time by the finish were running out. Rolling down with a shut throttle towards the control, Graham opened up as we crossed the bridge – and it mis-fired. It cleared, but from then on anything other than fairly high revs would cause it to cough and stutter. Just what we needed!

"Bloody mag! It's always the bloody mag on Squariels." Graham wasn't happy. The chaps on the control were concerned for us, asking what the problem was – they'd heard the loud misfiring as we approached – but there was nothing they could do to help of course. Mind you, it was a bit difficult talking to them with Graham keeping it revving fast rather than letting it stop!

All we could do was keep it revving and finish. So it was back through Strasswalchen again – we had passed there on the way out that morning – and back into Salzburg to clock in at the Zelkontrolle. All our troubles had gained us a total of 58 penalty points – and that was only the first day!

Once we were in the parc firmé I stuck my head behind the engine to have a look at the magneto – and gosh it was warm down there. Not the ideal place to keep all the windings' shellac insulation cool, but that's just the way it was and there was nothing I could do about that. Just about the only thing I could do was to check the points and the distributor – which seemed just fine. I cleaned the points a bit, polished the rotor arm and hoped...

We were soon turfed out of the parc anyway, so we made our way up to our hotel, caked in dust and sweat and really looking forward to a good wash and change, before going back into town to eat and catch up with the first day's news.

The Army teams were all billeted in the Hotel Pitter so that's where we headed, although we were both pretty tired I'll admit. However we just had to hear how the others had got on, so that's where we started. Geoff was already there.

"Graham – there you are! How did you do? Not seen hide nor hair of you all day."

"Hello Geoff. No, we were set off after you. Had a bit of bad luck today, but we'll make it up tomorrow. Have you seen Colin or Ron this evening? No, not Rogers, Edge - Colin Edge. I was wondering how the rest of our team have done." But Geoff hadn't seen either of them so he told us about how he'd done, which was very well and all three of them in the 'Beam team still had clean sheets!

"But enough of us – how did you do? Bad luck you say – what happened?" and Graham gave him a brief resumé of our day's misfortunes, but just then Jackie Wood came over – he was in the Army's 'A' Team on one of their fancy new 500 Beezas. I'm afraid that Graham and I felt a bit left out for a while as Jackie, Fred Rist and Paddy Doyle, all on BSA M24s, had also lost no marks at all that day. So there was another Brit team with clear cards with which to start Day 2. I congratulated them - and meant it, as before the event I'd had my ear bent by a few of the German support crews, or Technische Sportgruppe as they were called, about how this time they would be sweeping the board. So I was pleased that we were giving them a good challenge – even if Graham and I weren't with them up at the top.

Mind you, as I've already said, some of the other army types had come a cropper. Apart from Berry and Smith crashing, Lt. Riley's tank had split on his Norton, so the army's 'B' and 'C' teams had already blotted their copy books.

"What did you make of Linz then?" said Geoff. We had to think back, as to me at least it was already becoming just a bit of a blur of endless miles of dusty roads with towns and villages flashing past, interspersed with brief halts at the time controls. But then I remembered that, although there had been no Control at Linz, they had closed the main street to all other traffic.

"Blimey, that was something like the Isle of Man wasn't it, scorching through the middle of town!" As if we hadn't been there ourselves and couldn't even imagine it, he was again flat on the tank with his right elbow way down as he held the throttle wide open. Maybe he'd already had a drop of lager, but the adrenaline was also still in there somewhere.

"That was really great – and they were all waving at us from the windows too. Well, it was great 'til a blooming great dog decided to cross the road in front of me! I missed the back of it by inches – made it hurry up a bit I can tell you. Mind you, those railway lines were a pain too and Alan told me later that his front tyre suddenly wanted to follow the tram lines, but he got it away and he didn't do that again. Marj was alright though." I didn't remember anything like that when we went through, but then perhaps it had been different for us on an outfit?

Someone spotted Marjorie across the room and Geoff waved her over to join us and got her a drink - orange juice it was. But no, she'd had no trouble with railway lines either, but what she really wanted to talk about was extending her 'holiday' afterwards and riding into Yugoslavia, somewhere she'd never been to before. She said that three of them were game for it and was there anyone else interested? I'm afraid that most of us had to get back to work afterwards, but it did sound fun at the time.

I suppose that my earlier reservations about being amongst such esteemed company in such an elite event were resurrected at about that point. After all, Geoff and Marjorie were in the Sunbeam teams, while in their Team A there was Len Heath and Bill West on their Ariels, together with Colin Rogers on his Enfield – all of whom were also in the Silver Vase Teams.

82

Perhaps unsurprisingly, none of them had lost any marks so far, nor were many of them to do so all the way right up until the very end as it turned out. That's why I was still somewhat in awe of the company I found myself in. Mind you, their Team C had not done so well, with Toomey's Panther having let him down, so he'd retired and a few points were lost elsewhere too. So Graham and I weren't entirely on our own.

The CSMA team was there as well and Les Ridgeway was suffering from a grazed cheek, so Graham asked him about it. He'd been passing a farm gate at some speed on his Goldie when a dog ran out in front of him. Dogs, gravel and hay waggons seemed to be blighting that year's event! Anyway, he ran over it. Well, it probably damaged the dog more than him, but he slid down the track on his face, while the bike bent its 'bars and smashed the twist-grip, just like Graham Berry had done just a little earlier in the day. I suppose he'd only felt the damage to his face later because meanwhile he'd heaved the 'bars about straight, fought off the farmer, tied the throttle cable to his thumb, and rode on. He even got to the next control on time! What a stout fellow.

Les also mentioned Billy Tiffin, who was on his 350 Velo in both the Silver Vase Team A as well as the West of England MCC team. He was much on his own though, as Goodman, the boss of Velocette at Hall Green in Brum, had decided not to go for the Inter that year. As a result, Billy's was the only Velo entered - although there were a couple of 'em in one of the Dutch teams. Anyway, he'd gone a purler on a gravelled bend. He wasn't hurt, but a rock had badly bashed his petrol tank and split it. He'd fixed it temporarily and was game for Day 2. Hmm - come to think of it now - I wonder if John Goodman had chickened out of the Inter because of all the worries about Germany at the time? He was called Johannas Gütgemann originally you know... Anyway, it doesn't matter now.

Quite few solo riders had mishaps on those road surfaces, and we'd drifted a bit on a few bends as I've said, but it wasn't like pranging a solo at speed, so having three wheels was an advantage sometimes.

We met more charioteers that evening. One of the private entrants was there with his young son and they joined us at table for dinner that evening, where he introduced us.

"May we join you? Thank you. I don't believe we've met - I'm Dr. Galloway and this is my son, William" and the boy politely said hello, whereupon we introduced ourselves too. "Will is riding shotgun for me, aren't you lad?" and he laughed. It turned out that the boy, he must have been only 12 or 13 or so, was very keen on Westerns, the cowboys & indians films that were all the rage around that time, and had recently been taken to the cinema by his father to see 'Rough Riders Round-up', with Roy Rogers in the lead role.

I said it all sounded really rather rumbustious, but Graham didn't think it was very funny - but then maybe he didn't appreciate alliteration? Oh well, we all got on quite well over dinner anyway. Looking back, it must have been quite an experience for a schoolboy to be taking part in such a high status international event with his father. Certainly very educational and character forming, if rather amazing. I wondered what his mother had thought of it?

They'd had problems too that day though. The sidecar body had tried to part company with its chassis. Luckily, they had managed to find lots of copper wire and had used it to bind the body back onto the chassis, but he wasn't very confident about it's security and permenance.

"Wouldn't want to lose my passenger, would I? No, we'll decide in the morning, but it really does need something of a rather stouter form of attachment I'm afraid. We'll see, eh lad?"

After hearing all about that as well, our troubles seemed minor and should have been dealt with as a matter of course, but that's not how it turned out for us. No matter, after quite a good meal and a few beers – oh, it was only their thin lager, but it was cold and very thirst quenching so we didn't grumble – we cheered up and were looking forward to the second day's riding. Monday had been 295 miles, while Tuesday was to be only 230, but we'd been told that it would be a fair bit tougher, going east through Salzkammergut and up into the Dachstein mountains. Otto had told me that the lakes were very beautiful and I was hoping to have a few spare seconds to get a glimpse.

However, I never did get to see them.

Report Of The 1st Day of the 1939 ISDT by von Gustav Mueller
from *Das Motorrad* 2nd Sept. 1939

"There were a lot of defects already on the first day, and a number of retirements, too. The biggest experience of that first day had been that loose gravel does not have the same frictional coefficient as a nice rough asphalt surface, and so a lot of people already had gone to the ground. The English private riders lost a whole clutch of men, but also the Italians and we too did lose some riders. Anyhow, the affected English riders were more or less unknown people, who may not have been aware what a six days trial in Germany's mountains stands for!"

"As always, this ISDT has generated a new 'technical term'. It came from our great creator of new terms, national rider Otto Sensburg. From then on, our riders said, when they had gone into hedges or onto the ground: 'Da hat's mi überlisted' = 'There it did outwit me!' And that is a pretty figurative saying. That day it did outwit many riders and this always happens at the beginning of an ISDT, as one does not find one's 'speed' straight away. Here in Ostmark (Austria), with its dust and gravel and the never ending bends, it is something very special..."

When the Final Report was published, which very few of the British competitors ever got to see, the records stated that No.39 had retired at Vocklamarkt Zeitkontrol with 98 penalty marks.

Quite why Oates' understanding of his penalty and the notes of his performance in the event differs so much from the later official records is not now known. However, Oates being officially retired early turned out to be irrelevant in the end, despite their expectation to continue on Day 2.

CHAPTER 8

- in which the day fails to go as expected

"**WERE YOU** in a team Granddad?" Andy is still trying to get his head around a quite unfamiliar scene, it being nothing like he's ever experienced himself, or ever heard of before really.

"Oh yes, we were South Liverpool MC, one of the top teams y'know – not just anyone could be in it!"

"So how many were there in a team?"

"Three. But then the A-CU had two teams – and the Army, they had three teams, together with their boss and lots of support crew, plus Joe Acheson who was their back-up rider. Poor old Joe, he went all the way there and never got to ride."

"Oh well, not just anyone could be in the club teams then? First come, first served was it?"

"No no, the teams were selected – oh yes, only the very best got in! Although..." and Eric peters out when he realises that it hadn't really applied to him.

"Were you selected then, Gramps?"

"Er, yes – Graham selected me" he says quickly, carrying swiftly on. "Anyway, in our team there was Ron Clayton on his 350 Triumph, Colin Edge on his 350 Matchbox and Graham and me of course. We had no team manager or TSR like Geoff, Alan and Marjorie had in the Sunbeam Club team, but then they were going for the Hühnlein Trophy. No, we were just in for the Bowmaker Trophy, along with all the other clubs. Mind you, Colin was also in the Matchless factory team, so he had twice the load on his shoulders. But then, he had his fiancé, Peggy, along with him to cheer him up."

"What? He brought his girlfriend along? Was she in the team too then?"

"Oh no, she was just watching, but there were lots of spectators. There was Lavinda to start with, and then there was..."

"Right, OK, so you had groupies too, but let's cut to the chase - you'd had problems on the first day, but how did you get on the next day - Tuesday was it?"

"Yes, Tuesday - Day 2. Well, it wasn't so good..."

We were up early the next morning and down to the parc to see if the magneto was coming out to play, but it seemed it wasn't. Nothing. Oh, there was a spark, but it just wouldn't start, although Graham was adamant that it was an intermittent fault in the mag. I stripped it down as far as I could before our start time, but still couldn't find anything. I'm not really a mechanic, I was just Graham's ballast, so he had another look at it himself.

"It breaks down under load..." he told me, whatever that meant, and stood there shaking his head - but then we were called to the Start.

So we missed out from then on. They all went off and we cheered and encouraged them – they were doing it for us as we were out of the game.

I was pretty fed up once we were left alone in the parc, but then Gustaf and his pal Otto came over. Once their own riders had all gone they were presumably at a loose end for the rest of the day, until getting back into action when they all returned.

"Hullo Eric, was ist das problem?" and so I explained – and admitted that we couldn't seem to fix it. I suppose it was no surprise that they saw it as being a challenge to their Technische skills and they insisted on us letting them 'haben Sie einen Blick'.

Well, Graham and I didn't get a look in for the next half hour and our lame duck was just covered in grey overalled figures either helping or taking the opportunity to closely inspect a square-four engine. It was all rather funny really, seeing those Germans working on our Ariel, with all sorts of bits of engine briefly being waved about - but having missed the Start we were past caring.

Then one of them finally managed to successfully kick it up, which was encouraging. They fiddled with the slow-running jet adjuster whereupon it even ticked over well. It was stopped and then started again easily, as it usually always did, and stayed clean as they revved it. Blimey – they'd fixed it!

Gustaf then explained to us that it had them puzzled initially, but they came to the conclusion that it wasn't the fault of the magneto at all and so they looked at the carburettor. It turned out that it was a blocked idle jet, which is why it wouldn't run at low revs. Obvious really, but we were convinced all along that it was the mag and not the carb. Well, Graham was anyway. I didn't know.

Anyway, we were back in action - but with nowhere to go.

Otto said he knew where we could get good Kaffee und Kuchen, so that gave us somewhere to go and we wandered off in that direction with Graham offering to get it by some way of a thankyou to our German friends. We bumped into Peggy and Lavinda and they joined us. It turned out that it was just tea and pastries really, but that was just fine. It did seem rather strange sitting there, relaxing in the sunshine, when we should have been hammering our way through the Salzkammergut and, as Graham sadly pointed out, we would have been approaching Steinerkirchen by about then. However, having cheered ourselves up a bit with the cream cakes, and with it already turning out to be another stinkingly hot day, it was then that Gustaf suggested that we all went for a swim in the river.

Now neither of us had our costumes with us – swimming wasn't at all what we had expected to be doing that week – but Gustaf brushed that aside with something about good health and fitness eclipsing any prudery, and going on about it a bit, but it was all in German and we weren't very interested anyway. But for some strange reason the girls didn't want to join in so they left us and we went down to the river upstream of the town where there was a backwater away from the very fast flowing Salzach River. We stripped off quickly and Otto dived in, turning back and encouraging us. Well, I dived in, surfaced, and found that I couldn't exhale – it was SO cold! It must have been over a minute before I could make myself start breathing again, the thermal shock was really so great. I swam about a bit just to show willing and keep our end up, but climbed out well before the others did, collapsing on the bank - and steaming as thankfully the sunshine was quite warm by then. I then realised of course that the river was mostly melt-water from the mountains where the glaciers were busy shrinking in the summer. The others eventually got out too, declaring just how bracing it was and how a good cold beer was what was needed next. I didn't object to that bit.

The rest of the day drifted by, later meeting up with Peggy and Pat in the Bier Keller, and then Lavinda, Peggy, Connor and Miriam came in too, so it was quite a party for a while. We had to explain our misfortune yet again but then got onto what we would do the next day, Wednesday. Graham and I were pretty much free agents by then of course, although some of the others had to be on call both before the start and on their riders' return.

Otto was adamant that the very best place to watch the action would be at the top of the Grossglockner Pass, telling us to watch out for 'Wiggerl, auf seiner BMW-Gespann', whoever or whatever that might be. However, that would mean a very early start in order to avoid getting in the way of the competitors. I'd heard of the pass before and was keen to see it – or experience it more likely. Oh, I'd expected to see it from the sidecar of course, but as a spectator I'd see much more and still ride up there too. For some reason Graham wasn't so keen and it struck me that it would be to my advantage as I could really experience it by riding up there on my own machine.

It wasn't long before we heard the first of the riders arriving back in town, our German friends having already left to be back on duty. We walked back to the parc fermé and watched the travel-stained riders return, looking very weary, hot and dusty. Connor was looking out for Chris Bates on his 350 BSA, but it seemed that he was late. Chris did eventually turn up with no problems, he'd just found it unexpectedly difficult keeping to time. We were waiting for the other two in our team of course and Ron's Triumph was running flat when he came in, but he'd fixed the slipped timing by the time he started the next day and he was doing well. So was Colin, although Peggy said he was not feeling too well and they went off to their hotel almost directly and we didn't see him again until the next day.

So of course there were lots of things going on there as the machines collected on the hard standing, with plugs being cleaned, carbs adjusted, oil checked and topped up, repairs and adjustments made and quite a few tyres being changed and so the Dunlop boys and the chaps from Continental, the German tyres, they were all busy too.

We must have gone in for dinner after that although I don't recall much about it, but then we caught up with some of the other news in the bar. Jackie was there again, and once more had got a clear round. Not so some of his army team mates though, as the three 500 Nortons in their Team B all seemed to have weak tanks. Riley's tank hadn't stayed fixed and he'd run out of petrol in the mountains, having to be brought back later on. Sargeant Dalby's tank was also leaking so he'd had to fill up at every opportunity, while Corporal Berry's tank had split really badly, so he'd had to retire. Norton tanks were soft-soldered.

The Army's tales got worse, as it seemed that Team C's Matchlesses hadn't fared much better. Poor old Smith, who had battled to repair his front forks after the crash on Monday, had finally given up and retired as his machine just wouldn't go in a straight line. Sargeant-Major Mackay had suffered a spill and smashed his headlamp and bent the number plate, but thankfully that was all and so he and Davies were able to carry on.

So their hopes all depended on their Team A, which was still in pretty good form and still doing very well.

Some time after that, Fred Perks from the CSMA team arrived in the lounge, looking a bit out of sorts. It seems that he'd got back to the Austriahof, where he was staying, with a hot bath being highest on his agenda. He said that his shoulders had been aching, while his wrists were beginning to swell - and then he fell asleep in the bath! He'd only just got down and wanted something to eat. Someone went off to see if something could be rustled up for him while Norman got him a drink.

"God that was tough today, wasn't it? Those roads, or tracks rather, played hell with my shoulders - same for you?" Some of the riders agreed with him, nodding wryly. "And did anyone else see that BMW by the side of the road up over the top of the Gschütt Pass? He'd completely knocked a head and barrel right off his engine - must have hit a rock or something. If a thing's worth doing, it's worth doing properly, what?" No-one in our group had seen that, but it seemed that quite a few Germans had retired that day, judging by the number of dead machines they had seen.

"I never did think it were a good idea havin' your pots sticking out the side like that, it's just askin' for trouble on tracks like these." Jackie's strong opinions were made for sharing, although he too had missed seeing the wreckage. "Silly idea, it's much better to do it like Douglas do - fore 'n aft - if you've got to have a flat twin at all, that is!"

91

Geoff was there too and he was about to tell us all about his adventures through the day when Faron and his pal spotted us from across the lounge, waved, and came over to join us. They'd done well that day and were pretty cheerful, bringing a couple of beers for us with them. Graham introduced everyone and then Geoff finally got to telling us how the day had gone for him.

"They were really tight on the timings, weren't they? I mean, three minutes lee-way at the controls is fair enough, but they were being really strict about it today. Given the rough roads out there today it made it very difficult, what? And did you see that poor bugger who went off the road and way down into the lake! Just past one of the Bads I think, but we went past so many Bads today I've lost track - maybe it was Bad Alm? Anyway, I saw him swimming back so he'd survived. Nice day for a swim, eh?" Graham and I just smiled at each other.

"Ach, das was Heinrich und Wolfgang! Und they verloren, er, lost, their Zundapp Gespann!" It must have been Faron's friend that Geoff had seen in the water.

"An outfit? So there were <u>two</u> of 'em were there? Did they both get out?"

"Ja, unverletz", replied Faron's friend, nudging him in the ribs and laughing - clearly there was more to the story, but they didn't share it with us and so Geoff got on with his.

"But then George and I were going up the Gschütt Pass, heading for the St. Koloman Kontrolle, and do you remember just how close it was to the edge, Jackie? No fences, nothing apart from sheer drops down to the valley way below." At this point I noticed Faron and his pal exchanging meaningful glances and nodding - it must have been tough for everyone up there.

"Well, we were told that the Pass would be closed to traffic weren't we, but oh no, round the bend we went and there was a bloody great lorry in the middle of the road! George went one side of the lorry and I went the other – it was a choice of being squashed or lost! I went on the outside and I tell you no lie, my front tyre was less than six inches from the edge... I think I stopped breathing for a bit." Geoff ran out of words for a moment as he remembered it so clearly. It would have been interesting if George, that's George Eighteen, if he'd been with us too, as he could have told us just how he managed to squeeze his 350 Matchless through the gap!

"Mind you, going back down was fun too, what with all the loose stones, ruts and the scary 300 foot drops on the side. I'll admit I was sweating a bit by the time we got down. But we did it, didn't lose a mark and here we are – anyone want another one of these lemonades?" and he waved across at the girl going round with the large jug of beer.

The nattering went on for a bit between all the chaps who had actually ridden that day, but then I saw Peggy and Lavinda across the room so I left Graham and the others to it and went over to talk to the girls.

"Hello again. Is Colin all right, Peggy?" I'd remembered them going off to their hotel early on, but there she was back down again.

"Yes, he's well enough I think, but he was very hot and tired so he's gone to bed early. I'll go back up soon."

"Oh, right. Making sure that he's ready for it tomorrow, very sensible. Talking of which, I was thinking about tomorrow – I'll probably set off early and try to get to the top of the Grossglockner Pass before the riders pass through. They say it's really worth seeing. Anyone fancy it?"

"Funny you should say that" said Lavinda. "Miriam and I were thinking the same – so we could ride together if you like? It really would have to be a very early start though!"

"Right ho, up before the birds it is! What do you think? About four o'clock then? They start setting off at five, so that should allow us enough head-start. You coming Peggy? I've got a pillion," but she showed no interest at all, probably wanting to see Colin off and be sure of being there to greet him at the end of the day.

Peggy left shortly afterwards and Lavinda and I talked for a bit about the rumours of what was happening on the Polish borders, before we too went our own ways to get enough kip for the early start.

Well, to try to anyway, because I'd only just got off to sleep when I was jerked awake by some idiot outside shouting something through loudspeakers on top of a van going along the road. I've no idea what it was all about, nothing to do with me anyway, and was trying to get to sleep again when next there was a heavy rumble of vehicles outside. I got up to take a look, but all I could see was a seemingly endless column of lorries, troop carriers probably, going past and out of the town. I didn't like the look of that at all, but there was nobody to ask about it so I went back to bed.

Allan Jefferies was in Britain's International Trophy as well as both the Triumph and the Bradford MCC teams and typically he arrived back right on time again, despite having gained a puncture half way round and fitting a new tube at the next control. He thereafter made all his time up, his 500 Triumph running well, so still having a completely clean sheet at the end of Day 2. After a quick drink of water back at the parc firmé, he then fitted a new front tyre and tube.

In Britain's Silver Vase team, Len Heath had also had to avoid a vehicle that day. The car was driving on the wrong side of the road and Heath had to take his 500 Ariel off the road and into the trees. Neither he nor his machine suffered from this and he finished the day with another clean sheet.

Also in the Vase team as already mentioned, Billy Tiffin's Velocette petrol tank was seriously damaged and still leaking petrol badly, despite an earlier repair. He arranged with the Dunlop people to blow his tank dry with their air-line and then applied sealing compound internally, but eventually it was unsuccessful and it finally caused his retirement.

Peter Chamberlain of the A-CU was involved in a contretemps in the parc fermé with one of the German officials who had stopped the crew of a BMW outfit attempting to straighten their damaged sidecar chassis with tools borrowed from a British team. The official said that they must only use their own tools, but Chamberlain knew that no such rule existed. The German riders were nevertheless disqualified, although it was then stated that "...the competitor has chosen to retire of his own free will..."

The Score Sheets posted at the Start the following morning showed that a further 24 riders had retired on the Tuesday, making a total of 39 so far. The majority were German and Italian riders, but as well as the four British Army riders this also included private entrants F. Fletcher on a 124cc Excelsior and Dr. Galloway on a 499cc Rudge outfit, whose repairs to the sidecar body proved unsustainable.

CHAPTER 9

- in which Austria's scenery is appreciated

"**SO WHAT** was so special about this 'Pass' you all went off to see?" While Andy can speak German reasonably well, he's never yet visited the south of Germany.

"Ooh it's wonderful, the Grossglockner Pass is. You've just got to see it yourself lad, no pictures can tell you what it's really like. We've got nothing to compare to it in Britain, I can tell you. Now, when you get your licence and then get yourself a real motorcycle, not that little Japanese egg-whisk or whatever it is you buzz about on at the moment! No, when you get a real steed, you go over and take yourself up there, then you'll see just what I'm talking about!" and Eric nods, confirming that there's no more to be said about it at this stage.

"OK, fair enough Gramps. It'll be something to look forward to I guess..." although he's not holding his breath, what with the cost of the next stage of the motorcycle test to get through, not to even think about that Student Loan millstone still hanging around his neck. So a decent bike is far enough away in the future at the moment, leave alone a long Continental holiday!

"Anyway, tell me all about it then - you and your girlfriends rode up there together, didn't you?"

"What do you mean - 'girlfriends'? We were just friends. Yes, we were all just friends. You do get a bit cheeky sometimes Andrew! You really should..."

"Only joshing, Gramps, only joshing. But c'mon, get on with it" - and indeed Eric would prefer to tell his grandson about his Great Adventure, rather than tell him off, so he sorts out just where he'd got to, and continues his tale.

I managed it - I did get up at about three-thirty in the night, with a quick splash and a drink of water as there was nobody else around to get me a cuppa. Still, I was feeling quite fresh so, stuffing an apple into my jacket pocket, I ventured out into a still very dark world.

As always, the Scott started first time, after the ritual tickle and a priming swing of the kickstart of course, and I trickled quietly down through the town to where the girls were staying, only to find them ready and waiting. The right sort, eh?

"Good morning ladies - or should I say Gutenmorgen Damen?" and they smiled and started their machines. Straight away it was obvious that Miriam's lights on her BSA weren't up to scratch. It looked like she'd got a sleepy glow-worm in there that didn't want to play, so I let Lavinda lead and I rode at the back, sandwiching Miriam between the two well lit machines.

After the now familiar daytime hustle and bustle of Salzburg, a city that was currently the focus of both the Festival and the ISDT while also getting on with its everyday business, it was all strangely silent as we passed through as quietly as possible. There were lights coming on around us however, presumably they were the competitors and officials getting up for the five o'clock start of Day Three.

Graham had the programme with him, but fortunately I still had the map that I had pulled out of the Green 'Un the week before I'd left, so we at least knew the general direction and the names of the towns and village along the route, and we could always ask.

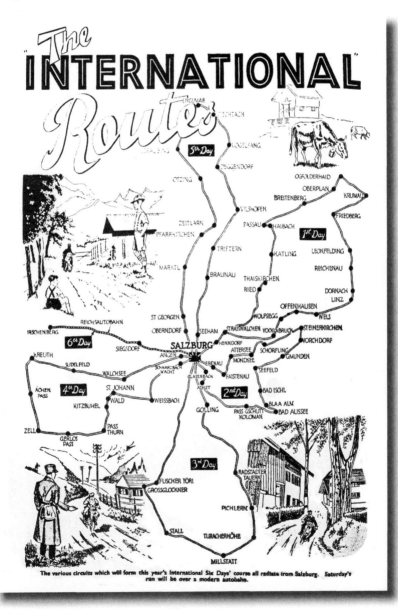

The various circuits which will form this year's International Six Days' course all radiate from Salzburg. Saturday's run will be over a modern autobahn.

97

The sky was brightening as we left the outskirts of the city and out through the shallow valleys heading due south. I must say it was all very pretty, being open and green with not many buildings apart from the occasional small village. No idea what all that 'Lebensraum' business was about - they seemed to have plenty of living space. We rode out through Kuchl and past Golling, where the competitors would have a Zeitkontrolle that day, and then to St.Johann im Pondau where we saw them setting up another Kontrolle.

So we were very cheerfully bowling along through a clear dawn which was promising another lovely day, having knocked the lights off some time before, although then watching out for somewhere for fuel. We passed Taxenbach and then Bruck with no luck, but with the mountains beginning to loom up ahead of us we knew we'd need filling before then. Lavinda dropped back alongside me and stabbed at her petrol tank, clearly she was concerned about it too, so when we arrived in Fusch and saw another Kontrolle being set up, we stopped. We asked them where petrol could be found and it turned out that we were in luck - there was a pump just down the road and they were opening early for the event. So we all three tanked up and carried on, with Miriam leading this time, although as we left I could catch just a tantilising trace of what smelled like fresh coffee coming out of a nearby window...

The Glockner Road was rising steadily along the Fuschertal, a lovely forest valley which also smelled just wonderful that morning. Oh to be on a motorcycle, out in the fresh air, riding through beautiful countryside along empty roads! I glimpsed a wheel to the left in the corner of my eye and turned to see Lavinda riding nearly alongside, grinning and waving her arm above her head, also taking it all in. It was good to be there.

And then we reached Ferleiten, where the Grossglockner High Alpine Road really began. The way steepened a bit, but the surface was good, quite wide and smooth, although with lots of tight bends - Otto had told me that there were about 40 of them! It all looked quite new so I asked about it later, after climbing the 14 miles or so and once we'd finally got to the top - well, as far up as we went that day anyway. We met a cheerful Austrian chap with good English who was also up there to watch, but I don't think I caught his name. He said that his father had worked on building the road from 1930 or so through to when it was finished just four years before we were there, so that made sense of it all looking so new.

However, he then told me that people had been crossing over the Alps on that route, through the pass between Austria and Italy that's nearly 8,000 feet high, for well over 4,000 years! I said that I didn't know how he knew that because, having ridden almost all the way up there I couldn't imagine walking all the way up it, over the top and then all the way back down again, leave alone with just a donkey to help me! However I'm afraid that he took offence at that, assuming that I thought he was making it all up, so he then explained at some length how his father's team of road-workers had found all sorts of ancient things along the way, including bronze knives, chains and shackles, some gold jewellery and even a Roman statue near the top. I thanked him and buttoned my lip after that. Fortunately the first rider came through soon afterwards.

But going back to us riding up the High Alpine Road - well, it was just great. I'd done nothing like it before, or since come to that. It just kept on going up and up! We weren't pushing it, although it wasn't that steep at any point and we were able to keep an eye on the scenery - certainly I was seeing more of it than if we'd still been competing. The bends were quite smooth and the new road was far better than much of the stuff we'd been through earlier. The surface was made of neat, well laid sets which were very even and smooth as I said - but I'll bet they were not so good to ride on in the wet... But after weeks of good weather, riding up there was really great fun, as well as the joy of seeing all those stunning views as we climbed. In fact we were enjoying the bends even more as we got used to them, keeping the speed up and getting well banked over - in fact I had to work quite hard to keep up with the girls who were really good riders and clearly enjoying themselves.

The Scott was working well too and I even got it into top a few times, reaching over the tank to snick it into gear with clutchless changes and thinking myself to really be the bee's knees on the road! However, there were also quite a few really sharp hairpins too, so it was down a gear or two - at least one of them had to be done in first - and then winding it back up again, up and around the next bend to see what there was to see and deal with ahead. It wasn't relaxing, but it was wonderfully exciting.

When we reached the bottom of the giant glacier over to our right we slowed up and then stopped in a passing place, or layby or something, shortly afterwards. I'd never seen a glacier before and didn't realise just how really big they were. Or bright! In the morning light coming in low over the mountains, the ice just shone and made us squint. It's things like that which make you glad you're sharing it and I somehow wasn't surprised when Lavinda, standing next to me, squeezed my hand by way of just saying 'Isn't this great?'

Back on the road, it just kept it up - more and more wonderful mountain scenery, mile after mile, until eventually we reached Fuscher Torl, a small plateau with a strange pyramid sort of building by the side of the road.
We stopped near there, parked up and watched them setting up the Zeitkontrolle on the other side - all very efficient, it really was all being run like a large military exercise, with everyone in overalls labelled with insignia and always with someone clearly in charge. Not at all like the relaxed informal way we do it in Britain.

The views from there were just amazing and when we'd torn our eyes away from all the glimmering white mountain peaks almost surrounding us we realised that we could look down to see the glacier below, the one we had ridden up alongside. It didn't look quite so big from above, but it was still impressive. We could also see the top bit of the road too, appearing and reappearing as it snaked up the right hand side of the steep valley.
It was then that my new friend, while we were still friends, told me about the building of the modern road, the Grossglockner High Alpine Road. It seems that the stone pyramid was a memorial to all those who had built the new road over the six years, sadly some of whom had died in the process.

I didn't know that Miriam was a magician as well as being a very accomplished rider, but then she produced not a rabbit, but a Thermos flask of tea from somewhere! I'd no idea that she'd it tucked away, but then she was pretty experienced in these sort of events and clearly knew how to be prepared. Not quite the same as coffee though, as I'd quite got a taste for it by then, but it seemed that real coffee was in short supply for some reason. However, after our very early chilly ride, a cup of warm tea was most welcome. Not only that, but Lavinda had some biscuits she'd saved from the day before, so we had something of a breakfast after all.

We certainly heard the first of the riders coming up the hill. The officials at the Zeitkontrolle all jumped into action, not that there was much for them to do for a bit as he was still a fair way below us anyway, but the morning was so quiet and clear that sound travelled very well. Then we glimpsed him rounding a bend below, before heading up much closer, with the crack of his exhaust echoing off the hillsides. He swung into the control and stopped without killing his engine - it was clearly very hot after the fast climb and maybe he didn't want to risk restarting it. That first rider was an Italian on what looked like a Gilera single, but we weren't too close, wanting to keep well out of the way.

A blip of the throttle, a brief wave and he was off again, accelerating hard and really looking very good. Quite how he'd got such a headstart over the others I don't know, but then a few minutes later more appeared and it soon got busy, with the NSKK chappies doing their stuff at the Kontrolle and some of the spectators cheering for their country's riders.

A couple of German riders were up next, both on BMWs. Numbers 35 and 38 they were, so they must have been Forstner and Lodermeir from one of the Silver Vase teams, or so it says in my old and battered Programme.

We saw Fred Whitehouse log in and then Fred Perks, both from one of the CSMA teams and both on their BSAs. Then there was a Dutch BMW outfit swinging up round the top bend, it must have been Herman Zuur. It was probably the first combo we'd seen arrive and it made quite a contrast to all the solos. It did make me wonder quite what it must have been like if, as in previous years, there had been some Morgans in the same class? Oh, they'd have the same number of wheels and possibly similar engines to some of the outfits, but not a lot else in common. Now they would have been a real contrast! However, it seemed that their day had passed and there were none entered that year.

I knew that before long the remaining two of our team would be coming through and we'd assured Peggy that we'd look out for Colin, but there was no sign of him. We were beginning to get a little worried when two riders came up together quite fast and it was Colin on his Matchless, together with a German on an NSU. By then we realised that we could get quite close to the Kontrolle without getting in the way and Colin spotted me while they were having their cards stamped. He shouted that he thought Ron Clayton, the third one in our now defunct team was behind him. However, Colin was also in the Matchless team, going for the Manufacturers' Trophy, so he was still a team member as well as going for an award himself. With a wave, he was off again.

No. 165 A.Eisenmann NSU 500 NSU Werke Team
No. 166 Colin Edge Matchless 350 S.Liverpool MC and Matchless Teams

After a bit, Miriam suggested that we should go down to one of the hairpins to watch them there, so we left our gear by the machines and walked really quite a way down until we came to the tree line, keeping well off the road of course. I'm afraid I regretted it later when we had to walk all the way back up again! However, we got to a tight right-hander and met up with an English fellow who had parked his car there earlier on. We introduced ourselves and it turned out that he was John Woodhouse, or Jack as he was usually called, who owned a garage in Cologne specialising in top British cars and motorcycles, mainly Bentleys and Broughs and the like, but others too. He was good company and so there was plenty of interesting nattering going on between watching the action. His Bentley drophead was parked inside the bend and during a gap between the riders going past we went over there, whereupon he offered us a nip of brandy which didn't go amiss at all.

Not only that, but he then dug out a Primus stove and brewed us all a pot of tea, together with plying us with some lovely fruit cake that he said that his housekeeper had made for his expedition. So there we were, the four of us having a lovely English picnic in the Austrian Alps, and very nice it was too.

No.27
Len Heath
Ariel 497cc
Silver Vase and
Ariel Teams

Refreshed, we walked back up part of the way to another corner and it was there that we saw Marjorie come past in great style. We spotted her very identifiable white cotton head-gear first, showing up in the bright mountain sunshine, and then her usual big smile as she swept past showed us that, as usual, she was really enjoying herself.

No. 255 Marjorie Cottle Triumph 249cc
Sunbeam MCC Hühnlein & Bowmaker Teams

I must say that she looked good, what with the tails of her loosened riding coat flying out behind her and the Triumph on full song, sounding right on key and going really well. I'm sure she didn't see us waving at her as she was naturally fully concentrated on the road, but no matter, we were cheering for her.

Another solo Ariel came up soon afterwards, Jaap Fijma in the Dutch Vase team sweeping very cleanly though the bends. Then almost immediately afterwards the Flook brothers took quite a different line, swinging wide round the bend on their Norton outfit and looking equally smooth, confident and cheerful.

Well, they were looking cheerful until a German rider on a solo cut past on the inside! Harold Flook didn't look best pleased and it made us gasp too a bit I must say.

No. 249 Harold and Andrew Flook Norton 596cc
International Silver Vase and Sutton Coldfield & North Birmingham AC Teams
No. 246 G.Ilgenstein DKW 250 NSKK Team C

We then carried on climbing back up, perspiring in the warm mountain sunshine, and came back to a quite fast left-hander where we stopped for a bit. The view there was strikingly different and perhaps we should have listened to Lavinda when she'd wanted to stay there on the way down. Although it was quite a tight turn, it was fast because the camber was good if you cut into the inside of the bend, as most of them did. The fast riders were really worth watching as they took many different lines around the turn and it wasn't obvious which approach was fastest - each to his own I suppose, although I'm still not quite sure how I'd have done it myself. Mind you, each rider was seeing it for the first time and didn't have the chance to study it as we were doing.

No. 17   H.Fruth   NSKK Team A
According to the Programme, Fruth was riding a BMW 500, although not matching the photograph

We stayed there for quite some time and were pleased to see Geoff doing well, as were most of the remaining Army riders too. One of them even spotted us and waved, although Miriam then criticised him harshly for this! Wag Bennett was still in the game, if not as fast as some, but his Matchless sounded well. Better than many in fact, as the high altitude was making some of the less well prepared engines run very rich. However, George Eighteen's 350 sounded good too so, together with Colin, the Matchless team were all going strong.

Soon afterwards, Whitfield zoomed past on his solo 500 BMW, closely followed by A-CU team mate Tim Blockley on his 500 Beesa, whom we'd met previously and who'd impressed us by his capacity for German beer. But then, having turned to see who was coming up next, we heard a short screech and then a dull thump behind us. We jerked round, just in time to see Tim flying though the air and landing on the grassy embankment. We rushed up, the girls looking to him while I dragged his machine off the road, trailing both oil and petrol behind it.

Well, Tim wasn't with it at all, sadly not even appreciating Lavinda's comforting chest, so he must have been well away. His loss, sadly. Anyway, I went back to try to get some of the oil off the cobbles with my handkerchief, but to no great effect. However I did my best, but I'm afraid that his machine was well and truly bent and clearly not fixable.

He'd over-cooked it on the sharp right-hander that immediately followed the fast left-hander and had hit the kerb. Presumably the bike had flipped, throwing him off, which was the bit that we had seen, and then bouncing back into the road, gaining bent forks and things. Tim had certainly retired.

Y'know, I've no idea what happened to his wrecked BSA. It could still be there for all I know.

I returned to see if Tim had survived. Thankfully he had, and was sort of sitting up, with Jack's hip flask at his lips, although I fear that he wasted more of it than he appreciated.

Then, when Tim could just about stand up, the girls got him up the bank a bit, settled him down, and we waited until the last riders had passed through the Kontrolle and Jack could take him back to Salzburg in his car.

Jack went back up to the top first in order to pick up his pal Bob Holliday, who was at the control, but we then had to wait until what the officials thought was the last of the riders had come up the hill, although there hadn't been anything through for some while. Y'see, with Tim on board, we had to go back down the way we'd come up, it being a much shorter way back than going on around the day's official route. It was a shame really because we heard later that the views from right up on the Grossglockner spur after they'd left us were stunning, while they said that the ride down through Rangersdorf, Grosskirchheim and to Stall was really lovely too. Ah well, some other time we thought - but now I'll just have to take their word for it I suppose. Anyway, we eventually all got back safely, if rather later than we'd expected.

When we did get back and had handed Tim over to his team mates at Hotel Pitter, we went off to our digs to quickly get tidied up and meet up again back in the bar. Unfortunately by then we had missed dinner, but nevertheless managed to scrounge something to soak up the beer. However, there was nobody to talk to really because most of the Germans were clustered next to a wireless set in the corner. It was interesting to watch from a distance because, although we couldn't really hear what was being said, clearly some of it found favour with the Nazis there, who loudly called "Hoch, hoch!" to show their approval, while others, mainly the locals, hissed at it. The Brits had congregated over in the Hotel Bristol to listen to the BBC News at 9 o'clock, so we went over there to join them.

Miss Bunce from the ACU was there and Miriam quizzed her about the latest news. Apparently there was some high level meeting or other going on between the Germans and the Russians, but nobody was sure what it was all about, so we were none the wiser really. Jack phoned his wife back in Cologne, and he looked no happier on his return...

However there had already been increasing numbers of cables, telegrams and 'phone calls arriving at the hotels here, with those back home urging their husbands and sons to return as soon as possible and so there was a lot of discussion going on about it in the evenings. Thankfully Emily, my fiancé, hadn't nagged me so far, but quite a few of the others were already talking about cutting out and heading back.

Not the top dogs though, oh no, our Trophy and Vase teams were doing really well and stood a good chance of taking at least some of the big pots home with them again this time.

Then we heard that Lieutenant R.K. Money had received a telegram ordering him to report back to his regiment at once. Poor old Rick hadn't had a good time of it really. Being a keen and not unsuccessful trials rider, usually riding his own 500 Beesa, he'd applied to go for selection for one of the War Office's teams, but his CO had refused it! He told us that he'd been a bit annoyed about that and so had taken leave from his regiment, the Royal Engineers, and entered privately, riding under No. 42 and all at his own expense. Good for him, eh? But then he'd just been dragged back - and with a clean sheet so far too! Poor old sod, it just didn't seem fair on him, especially since all the Army teams were still there, happily looking forward to carrying on into Day 4.

I asked one of the hotel staff what all the fuss in town had been about the night before and he told me that the Salzburg Garrison had been put on alert earlier in the day and then late last night had been sent East. The waiter said that it was generally thought that they were heading for Poland, but they hadn't been told any details, just sent. He added that there were now a number of distressed families in the area...

And then a bit more real news surfaced, met with a gasp and much excited talking going on around the wireless - the French government, so the BBC reported, had just 'very strongly advised' all French nationals to leave Germany within 24 hours. Well that was a turn up for the books. Nothing vague about that - although nothing to do with us either, as we knew of no French competitors taking part anyway.

Nevertheless, there was much more discussion and debate going on, as you can imagine, but no more actual facts were forthcoming and so someone then suggested going over to Hotel Pitter to see if the Army had more news? Presumably if there was a real scare going on, the Army would know about it first, so some of us went over to see. But no, they'd received no orders and were planning to ride as per usual the next morning.

The CSMA team were also there, looking pretty dejected I must say. Len Ridgeway had arrived late at a control that day, probably still suffering from the results of Monday's fall, and he had been docked 11 marks. This spoiled the team's sheet which had been clean up 'til then. Ironic really, as hitting the dog on Monday and bending the handlebars hadn't cost him anything at all that day.

However, what was worrying them even more was what had happened to Norman Blockley, their TSR? He'd not turned up that afternoon, but one of the German riders then told them that he'd seen Norman at the side of the road, apparently having crashed. Their Team Manager, Tom Davies, was really worried, getting no information or help from the organisers. Tom thought that he should go upstairs and tell Norman's brother about it, but was told that Tim was hard fast asleep after his bump on the head and that it would wait 'til the morning, when they might have learned more about the situation.

Lavinda spotted Will looking a bit fed up in the corner, so she went over to talk to him, then calling me over to hear the news. Sadly they'd had to retire and had spent the day properly repairing the sidecar. Even worse, his friend Billy Tiffin had finally given up and retired too, although he had since managed to effectively seal his tank at last. His father and Billy had decided to quit and go home together via Switzerland, doing a bit of sight-seeing along the way. It was indeed proving to be an educational holiday for the boy.

With nothing more to be learned we had a night-cap and then pushed off to bed. Oh, I wasn't sure what we'd be doing on the Thursday, but we'd think of something.

Fortunately my sleep wasn't interrupted by loud noises and the vibration of passing lorries that night, just by dreams of seemingly impossible trials sections...

CHAPTER 10

- in which most of the British riders leave

"**WHEN WAS THAT** again, Gramps? Late August - the 23rd?
Hmmm, that was when they conned the Soviets into thinking they
were safe, wasn't it? It was the Ribbentrop-Molotov Pact, which the
Nazis then went back on and invaded Russia. Bonkers! Y'know, it's
amazing really - I learned something about all this at school, and then
in a lot more detail at Uni, but I never thought that my granddad,
sitting here right on our doorstep, had actually been there - on the
spot at the time! It's great - you're living history, you are Gramps!"
and Andy looks up at his grandfather, only to find that he's fallen
asleep in his chair, and is beginning to snore.

What is also quite remarkable is that the whole of the day has
passed by while he's been totally captivated by all the tales told to
him by someone he's always thought of as being his dear old, but
rather boring, ancient grandfather.

However, it is now quite late and really he's got to get him up to
bed. Despite all the heavy hints earlier on, they've both missed out
not only on the drink of beer that he was so keen to have in the
middle of the afternoon, but his supper as well! Andy really doesn't
mind as he's so pleased to see his grandfather enthusiastic about
something for once! It's a bit as he remembers him years ago, when
Andy was just a boy. So it's no matter that their supper has been
missed - all the company and talking has clearly worn the old boy
out and bed is what's needed now.

"Come on Gramps, up we get..." It's not the first time he's put
his grandfather to bed and hopefully not the last, so he knows what
to do and how to do it.
"What? Where're we going... Oh, Andy, it's very good of you.
Time for bed is it? It's been a long day, hasn't it. No! Not my left
one! Aaah - that's better. Right" and they eventually make progress
out into the hall, with the stairs to negotiate next....

"You're a good lad y'know, despite what they all say about you..."
'Never misses a trick does he?' thinks Andy, and smiles as they tackle the stairs.

"Oh, Andy, what about my night-cap then? You'll have a tot too, will you, son?" Part of the night time ritual is always a drop of malt so Andy reassures him that it'll be waiting for him when he's returned from the bathroom.

Having sorted him out, and shared a tot of whiskey with him, Andy goes back down, makes a quick 'phone call, settles himself down on the settee as oft times before, and then takes time to review the day's amazing revelations.

He never really knew that his grandfather had been an enthusiastic motorcyclist - certainly never owning one while Andy had been around. As for just pushing off to Germany, on his own, while another world war was brewing on the horizon, well, Andy wonders if he'd have been up to it himself?

Going back over it all in his head, he gradually drifts off to sleep.

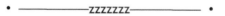

"Good morning Gramps! Here's your morning tea. Yes, it <u>is</u> morning, and no, I'm <u>not</u> disturbing you in the middle of the night - it's eight thirty and you're getting up once you're on the outside of that cup of tea." Andy has things to do before the weekend is out, but he does want to find out how the story ends...

So up, dressed and breakfasted, with yet another cup of tea by his side, Eric gets back to the plot.

There was still no news of Norman the following morning, but it seemed that the previous night there had been an agreement signed between the Russians and the Germans to the effect that they would never come to blows. Well, jolly good I thought, although not everyone saw it that way it seemed.

By the time we were up and about, many of the riders had started on Day 4's stage, heading south west into the Austrian Tyrol. It was going to be another long run, about 290 miles through the mountains, so Graham and I thought we'd make a relaxed late start and head out along their return route to watch them on their way back, say at Walchsee or somewhere. We'd ask someone about the best place to get a good view. Oh, and we had heard that Tiffin and the Galloways had left for Switzerland, going off to see the scenery probably. Touring.

So we stretched our legs in the town for a bit and then stopped for a tea or something at about 10 o'clock or so. We found a pretty little Kaffeehaus in the square, with one of the tables outside spare, so we plonked ourselves down and ordered a couple of coffees, hoping that they would actually taste like coffee, as some of those we'd had previously over there had been very strange. They duly arrived, and were fine, and by then we had got into conversation with a couple of locals.

I suppose we were pretty obviously *'Auslanders'* and so a couple of the locals soon wanted to talk with us. After we had explained why we were there - for the Inter, not the Festival - unsurprisingly, the conversation soon got round to the previous day's big news, the high level talks with the Soviet Union. I expressed the naive opinion that it would not have much to do with us in Britain, with which they agreed, but Graham hinted that, without the Russians to worry about, the Nazis could turn their attention west.... However, our new friends were quick to put us right about that.

"Nein! - it is only your press that tells that false story. We Germans do not want war with you again. We are friends - and your King, he is of German stock - so you will be best to join us. It is just the Französisch und die Juden that are the problem, but we can solve that together, you see." This was all presented quite forcefully, with both of them clearly of one mind, as if it was all quite obvious if you looked at it the right way.

Graham and I shifted uncomfortably in our seats - this was not at all to our liking, but then his friend tried to put us at ease.

"Ach, so now you will have no need to worry! We are friends - and there will never be any fighting between England and Germany while we have the Soviets on our side..." and the first chap nodded, assuring us that it was clearly the truth.

We were not at all sure about that either, there being more than one way to look at this argument. However, the two chaps were both so very sure of themselves, or of their digested politicians' spiel, that it really wasn't worth arguing with them just then, so we changed the topic and asked them about good places to visit in the Tyrol, especially with clear views of the riders' return route. However, they knew nothing of the Inter at all, leave alone Day 4's routes, so we finished our drinks, said goodbye and left.

"What did you make of all that then Graham? Were they saying that the Russkies would keep the peace? Can't see how they think that would necessarily be the case. I mean, what's in it for them? Trade, I suppose, because we do trade with them a bit - not a lot, but it's all good income and if their pals go to war with us, they couldn't maintain commercial relations I suppose?" Graham shook his head at this, having an even gloomier view of it.

"Or perhaps they were implying that we'd be too scared to take them both on at the same time!" I hadn't thought ot that...

"Hmm, well, let's hope it never comes to that!"

We wandered back to our hotel, bumping into the manager on the way in. He too had good English so we tried him about places to watch the day's return route. He was far better informed, but then most of his clientele were involved in the event so he knew a bit about what was going on. We showed him the 'Traject' map and he immediately pointed out where the big lake was, called the Walchsee, saying that it would be a lovely day to visit it. This made sense as it was on the competitors' return run and not too far away, so we thanked him and went up to our rooms to get kitted out, although for me it was no more than slacks, shoes and my leather jacket - it was indeed a lovely day.

However, I can't deny that the edge had been taken off it a bit by the conversation in the café with the two locals, who were presumably Nazi supporters...

Four days before, Soviet Foreign Minister Vyacheslav Molotov, on behalf of the Soviet Union, and Joachim von Ribbentrop, on behalf of Nazi Germany, had signed an 'Economic Agreement' which committed the Soviet Union to provide food products as well as raw materials to Germany in exchange for finished products such as machinery from Germany. This attracted little interest outside those two countries at the time, but it turned out to be very good planning as, during the first years of the war, this economic agreement helped Germany bypass the British blockade.

Then in the late hours of August 23, Ribbentrop and Molotov additionally signed the 'Nazi-Soviet Non-Aggression Pact' (also referred to as the 'Ribbentrop-Molotov Pact'.) Publicly, this agreement stated that the two countries would not attack each other, and this was the agreement that had made news further west. Superficially, it was just saying that if there were ever a problem between them, it was to be handled amicably. However, what was really meant by the terms of the pact was that if Germany attacked Poland, then the Soviet Union would not come to Poland's aid. Similarly, if Germany went to war against the West (especially France and Great Britain) over Poland, the Soviets were guaranteeing that they would not enter the war; thus not open a second front for Germany.

However, there was yet more under the surface. Unknown to the West, and further to this pact, Ribbentrop and Molotov then secretly added an Addendum (the existence of which was denied by the Soviets right until 1989). It was an extra agreement between the Nazis and Soviets to the effect that, in exchange for the Soviets agreeing not to join in with the possible future war, Germany was 'giving' the Soviets the Baltic States (Estonia, Latvia, and Lithuania). In addition, Poland was to be divided between the two, along the Narew, Vistula, and San rivers.

The obvious effects were that Germany would not have to fight a war on two fronts, while the new territories gave the Soviet Union a buffer state that it wanted in order to feel safe from any invasion from the West.

The 'Ribbentrop-Molotov Non-Aggression Pact' between Nazi Germany and the USSR sounded as impressive as it was eventually meaningless. The pact was supposed to last for ten years; it lasted for less than two.

We agreed that Walchsee would be a good destination, so dropping a bag of apples, bread rolls and a bottle of wine into the sidecar, we headed off west and out along through forests along the Inn Valley, keeping north of Kufstein and then along the shores of the large lake, sparkling in the sunshine. We really were feeling pretty relaxed, the disappointment of having to retire having now faded a bit with the challenging roads and wonderful countryside making a good job of compensating for it a little.

As planned, we were there before any of the competitors came through, so we didn't clash. We'd found ourselves a perfect spot up on an embankment on the outside of an apex of a long bend, with a good view both ways. It was ideal really. I had a bit of a snooze until the bark of an exhaust brought me back and I sat up in time to see a solo sweeping round the bend. It was sporting the red colours for Italy and was, I think, a Sertum - a 500 single. There were a couple more before a two-stroke came past - a little Puch it was, going very well indeed for such a tiddler.

Being there on an outfit ourselves, the occasional sidecar machine always caught our attention of course, and certainly the remaining big Zundapp outfits did look good. They had a very distinctive sound and seemed to be able to stay in top gear almost all the time. Oh, not up the mountain the day before of course, but along the valley where we were that day, their exhaust note barely changed as they swung round the bends, hardly slowing with their passenger hanging well out or belly down over the rear mudguard. Not that our outfits hung about! It was good to see the big Nortons and BSAs following through, but the other way around of course, so their line around the bends was different too.

They all had a good view ahead too, the land being fairly flat around there, so they had less chance of encountering a hay wagon on their side of the road! In fact, 'our' bend was very open so most them were using the whole of the road, much like they do at the TT on the Island.

It turned out to be a good day for us after all, munching our impromptu lunch in the sunshine, while watching a wonderful range of riders and machines hammer past us for a couple of hours.

Oh, the dust they raised tended to cover us a bit - and make the food a little crunchy - but that was a small price to pay for such good entertainment.

When we thought that probably the last rider had passed through, we fired up the Squariel and bumbled back to Salzburg. However, we weren't expecting to find all the fuss that was waiting for us back at the hotel. While we were away, and before most of the riders had returned, there had been a number of telegrams delivered.

Norton Motors Ltd, Bracebridge Street, Birmingham, United Kingdom
FAO ALL NORTON TEAM MEMBERS
WITHDRAW FROM EVENT STOP RETURN IMMEDIATELY STOP

There was also one from the British Manufacturers' Union which included the words "...BEAT A HASTY RETREAT..."

Well, this was all rather unexpected - and a bit extreme, surely?

And then, while we were chewing this over, yet another one was delivered, this time from the British Embassy in Berlin, strongly advising all British subjects to ".....CROSS THE SWISS BORDER A.S.A.P...." so it wasn't just the compeititors that were being called back...

While all this was being digested, the competitors were steadily arriving back in the parc fermé after a particularly hot, hard day, having ridden over 290 miles through the Tyrol and then along narrow, twisting dusty gravel roads through dark forests. Most of the Brits had done well though, so unsurprisingly all this bad news was the last thing they wanted to hear.

Very few of our lads had retired that day, although Les Ridgeway had to finally give up, with the throttle still being a real problem, his shoulder increasingly causing pain and his card collecting ever more penalties for late arrivals. Nobody blamed him for that and we were all impressed how he'd carried on for so long. However, Jack Breffitt had collected a puncture in the back wheel of his 350 Norton and then found he'd got a bent rear wheel spindle, preventing him from getting the wheel out and so having to be ferried back. Presumably his disappointment at having retired with a clean sheet was slightly eased by Norton's telegram. His other three Norton Team members wouldn't have been happy though, as Vic Brittain still had a clean sheet and, although the Flooks had been lumbered with 4 marks that day, they would still have been in the running.

In fact, the Flook brothers weren't happy at all about how they'd been treated, because they'd only been given 5 litres of petrol at the start and complained 'til they got 7 litres, which delayed their start. Then they ran out anyway.

However, somehow they cadged a bit more from a car driver, but they were still late at two controls, so got the 4 penalty points. They did of course immediately protest at the end of the day, but it wasn't allowed, leaving Germany as the only Trophy team still with a clean sheet. Ah well, nothing to be done about it, all things considered.

Our real disappointment though was to see Len Hall coming in on the back of a lorry. Geoff and Marjie's team mate had collected no penalties at all up 'til then, but late in the day he'd done a broadside on the gravel and slammed into a tree, badly bending his 500 Rudge and shaking him up considerably. What a shame.

So it was all rather gloomy over dinner that evening and then later in the bar, as most of the Brits were packing up to go home early the next morning. Not all though, as the Army hadn't received any orders to the contrary so they were expecting to bash on through Friday and Saturday as planned. Others were going to just finish it all off too, especially as quite a few were still doing well and had reasonable hopes of taking the odd gong home with them.

However, there had at last been news of Norman Blockley - he had indeed crashed and broken his leg. Not much more was known at that stage, other than that he would be delivered back to the hotel in the near future. Well, Tim and Tom were relieved, and meanwhile the CSMA team had agreed to battle on 'til the end.

You see, Hühnlein the Oberführer had been round, telling us that there was no need to 'run away' and promising that all who stayed until the end of the event would be ensured of having plenty of petrol - at which Harold Flook snorted loudly - and they would even be safely escorted to the frontier. Well, fair enough, quite a few of us were prepared to risk it, and the Army teams were still settled in, so we turned in that night intending to stay through to the end, probably pushing off either Saturday evening or on Sunday.

The British contestants recieve the announcement of the recall of their teams.
Nearest is Major Watling, a member of the ISDT Jury,
and next to him, and the tallest, is Peter Bradley, British Trophy Teams Manager.

With both their machines repaired, Tiffin and Galloway had already left together on Thursday morning, heading for the Swiss border and crossing at Martinsbruch. They had anticipated possible difficulties in obtaining petrol, so had acquired a 40 litre can which they had filled by decanting their tanks, which had already been topped up ready for the day's event, and then having their tanks filled as usual on the Thursday morning, despite neither of them still competing. The large can shared the sidecar with Bill Galloway, who had meanwhile been gathering other supplies, including cheeses, bread, some fruit - and had even topped up a Bocksbeutel with the red wine left in bottles scattered around from the night before, then bunging in a cork he'd also found.

The three of them stayed on Thursday night in a small Gasthof just on the Swiss side of the border, only to be called out by their landlady in the small hours to help at the Border Post. A small party of British riders had arrived, but it seemed that their papers were not entirely in order. It turned out to be the Ariel B Team, being Harold Taylor and Bill Peacock on their Ariel Square Four outfits, Buster Cunningham on his 500 Ariel, together with his wife and two others on solos. Dr. Galloway managed to convince the border guards that they were just as they had said, showing the guards the ISDT Programme with all the names listed. So, having been vouched for and passed through, they too were squeezed into the Gasthof.

It transpired that Taylor, a very experienced competitor with a works Ariel-Noxal outfit much the same as those ridden by both Oates and Peacock, had gone into a ditch late on Day 2 whilst avoiding an on-coming car. He was unhurt, but the Ariel's girder forks were badly bent and he had to retire. The forks were roughly repaired back at Salzburg and he was able to ride home. Peacock had retired on Day 1 for some now unknown reason.

Tiffin and Galloway rode on through Switzerland on the Friday, passing over the Fluella Pass and then spending the night at the village of Char. On Saturday they climbed the Oberalp Pass, where Galloway's sidecar yet again caused some trouble.

Approaching the top of the pass at a good pace, quite without warning the sidecar wheel came off, bouncing away up ahead, hitting and snapping a concrete pillar, but fortunately staying on the road from where it was later retrieved. The now two-wheeled-outfit then slid along the road's guard rail until it came to the end of it, whereupon it overturned, pinning Dr. Galloway underneath and ejecting his son from the sidecar. The machine came to a halt upside down, with its front-end hanging over a 1,200 foot drop.

Tiffin and the boy got the doctor out, righted the machine, refitted the wheel and happily carried on with their sight-seeing tour of Switzerland.

They eventually returned safely to England on the Velocette and the Rudge outfit, while the Ariel riders had arrived home slightly earlier.

BRITISH MILITARY TEAMS WERE TO COMPETE

Article from: *The Adelaide Advertiser, South Australia 24th Aug 1939*

"During this week the world's most important motor cycle trial, the International Six Days' Trial, is being held in Germany, and representatives from all motor cycle manufacturing countries astride their own machines are competing."

"The course runs through the Bavarian Alps and will pass through Berchtesgaden, where Hitler's mountain retreat is situated. Britain has held the International Trophy during the past three years, but following the advancement made in the manufacture of foreign machines, together with their performances in recent international road race meetings, sterner opposition is expected this year.

A number of European military teams, including three from Britain, were to meet for the first time in an international contest, and great interest has been evinced throughout Europe. Fifteen army motor cyclists were selected to undergo a course of training in readiness for the six days' event and went into a special camp on June 5. Although foreign teams have been similarly trained for several years, this is the first occasion that such training has been undertaken in England. At the end of five weeks' training, 12 riders were selected to continue the training and the three British army teams were selected from these riders. Physical training has been closely studied, and during the final weeks runs of 200 and more miles, with petrol stops, time checks on 'international' lines, trouble tests in between checks, and everything in line with the actual six days conditions, have been held. England's best scramble and trials riders have assisted and representatives of tyre companies have given instructions in tyre changing. The riders were stopped during their training runs and informed that they had a broken fork-spring, chain, puncture or other trouble, and they were then observed as they carried out repairs. During the final preparation days, the riders visited their respective factories for all information and instructions concerning their machines. The trial was arranged to finish on Saturday, when a cross-country test of rough riding was to take the place of the usual speed tests. German officials organised and controlled the competition and elaborate welcomes and entertainments were provided for the visiting motor cyclists."

"Four days of the International Six Days' Trial had been completed when the English team was ordered to return home. The course set down in German territory for this year's event was providing one of the most strenuous trials undertaken. At the end of the fourth day the British riders were satisfied that they would gain at least two of the major awards. so it was disappointing to all when the British riders withdrew. The Six Days event was in progress back in 1914 when war was declared and although the British riders were not in enemy country at the time, they experienced great difficulty in obtaining sufficient petrol to return to England."

"This famous trial is held annually in different countries. Germany organised the event this year running it towards the end of August in the Bavarian Alps near Salzburg. English clubs and manufacturers were represented by 12 teams and the British Army sent three teams comprising nine of its best motor cyclists. When the contest commenced from Salzburg the atmosphere was fairly tense but became more strained two days later when the Russo – German pact was signed. When only two days remained the British contingent decided to do their best to see the trial through. But late that night an urgent message was received stating that the British Consul in Germany had advised all British nationals to leave immediately. Early next morning they set out some for the Swiss and others for the French frontiers, recieving every help from the German authorities All eventually reached England."

"The trial finished with Germany as the winner and Italy the runner up."

Internationale Sechs-Tage-Fahrt 1939
Deutschland gewann alle Trophäen.
Die Ergebnisse:

Internationale Trophäe: 1. Deutschland (Seltfam-BMW, Sensburg-DKB, Fähler-DKB, Müller-Mayerhofer-BMW-Gespann) 0 Punkte; 2. Italien 43 Punkte.

Internationale Silbervase: 1. Deutschland (Forster, Linhardt, Lodermeier, alle BMW) 0 Punkte, 2:06:08; 2. Italien A O P., 2:16:18.

Adolf Hühnlein-Trophäe: 1. DDAC A-Mannschaft (Steinberger-Zündapp, Hahnmeyer-BMW, Charbonier-NSU) 0 Punkte 2:29:01;2. H-B-Mannschaft O P., 2:45:11,2.

Bowmaler-Trophäe: 1. DDAC München (Steinberger-Zündapp, Hahnmeyr-BMW, Köhler-DKB) 0 Punkte 2:22:19,4.

Die Große Medaille der FICM wurde nicht vergeben, da keiner der Bewerber strafpunktfrei geblieben ist.

The Published Results

CHAPTER 11

- in which a dash for home is made

"STREWTH, GRANDDAD, that was pushing your luck wasn't it? I mean, the war was just a few days off and you could have been interred for the duration!"

"Ah yes lad, hindsight is a wonderful thing, isn't it. But you see, we didn't know that the war was only nine days away, did we?"

Friday 25th August, 1939 **Day 5**

Marjorie had breakfast with Graham and me early the next morning and it soon became clear that we'd missed out on a lot of action during the night.

"About 1 o' clock last night Peggy was knocking on my bedroom door. 'We're off at five in the morning...' she told me. 'Good lord!' I said, 'Is Colin worse?', but no, she told me that there was going to be a war and that we all had to get out of the country! So of course I assumed that there had been some further news, but it turned out that no, there hadn't. It's just that they'd all been talking about it and decided that they weren't risking it and were going. Well, they've gone, in fact."

"Er, yes, it's pretty quiet here this morning isn't it. Nobody knocked us up though, did they Graham?"

"No. Not a squeak. Sneaked off without us. Bloody nerve. But come on, you're still here Marjie, why didn't you join them? And what are you doing today anyway?"

"Oh I'm riding of course! My start time is in about half an hour, so I'll just finish this pretend coffee and I'll get going. But just to fill in, I duly got up and did my packing - if we were all going to leave at 5am then I had to get ready. But then I said to myself 'This is daft! Here I am, about to go back to Coventry and say to Triumph that I'm sorry that I didn't do my bit and finish, because my friend Peggy said that there was going to be a war, so here's your bike back.' It didn't sound so good to me - they'd think I was a bit queer in the head - so I went out to look for someone who could tell me just what was going on, but there wasn't a solitary official around who would say anything. So I looked for one of our A-CU chappies, but no, they'd all gone - or so I thought."

"So then I thought the Army would know and so I dug out their boss, Charles Bennett - he was in his pyjamas but he let me in. 'Have you had your marching orders yet, Charles?' I asked, but no, he hadn't. Nothing. I told him I was game for staying until the end and was confident that I could get out when the time came. He said we should go to the top, so he pulled on his kit and we went over to General Hühnlein's office. Late as it was, he was there, still fully dressed in his uniform and everything and he warmly welcomed us in, kissed me on both cheeks and made a tremendous fuss, pumping Charles' hand and telling us that we were the only ones in our right minds, that the others were crazy to go. Everything would be all right and we should go back to bed to get a good night's sleep ready for Day 5's riding - and so, despite not getting much sleep at all, I'm off. See you this afternoon. Bye." And she was gone.

Despite their earlier advice, the Manufacturers' Union had later wired Major Watling, their representative at the event, with firm instructions to pack up and return, which he received late on Thursday.

British Manufacturers Union, London, United Kingdom
FAO MAJOR WATLING BMU AND ACU   STOP
PRESIDENT INFORMS THAT BRITISH CONSUL IN BERLIN HAS
RECEIVED INSTRUCTIONS TO WARN ALL BRITISH SUBJECTS
TO LEAVE GERMANY IMMEDIATELY   STOP

So Major Watling and Peter Chamberlain of the A-CU met with Baron von Falkenhyn to tell him of their new plans. He was most upset by it, but nevertheless produced a last bottle of champagne to toast the spirit of motorcycling comradeship, which struck a chord with them all. Chamberlain tore up Flooks' protest and they all parted on quite good terms, although the Baron may soon have been smarting over the £1 he had bet Graham Walker that there would be no war between Germany and Britain...

Despite many having left that evening, the Vase, CSMA and Sunbeam teams and others, had retired to bed with the intention of nevertheless completing the Trial. However, in the early hours of Friday the CSMA people were roused to be told that they were packing to make for the Swiss Border. Fortunately Tim Blockley had recovered well by then and Norman had been safely returned with his leg in splints, although without his BSA, which was lost without trace.

The competitors retrieved their machines from the parc fermé, thankful that their tanks had already been filled, and Fred Perks and Jack Breffit quickly got both their machines up onto Harold Tozer's trailer to save time. Perks was to drive Tozer's outfit while Breffit would drive Perk's Standard 9 car - not covered by insurance but needs must when the devil drives. Fred Whitehouse loaded his BSA back onto the sidecar chassis of his Ariel outfit. Chamberlain was with Peter Bradley in his large Delage saloon car, but for some now unknown reason Miss Bunce, the A-CU secretary, did not go with either Watling or Chamberlain and stayed on.

German officials were there, early as it was, continuing to insist that there would be no war, but despite their assurances the teams left for Innsbruck and then Switzerland, via Liechtenstein.

As Harold Flook expected, the promise of sufficient petrol came to nothing, but thanks to full tanks on both bikes and cars, together with 10 litre cans of previously foraged petrol and taking care with their fuel consumption en route, they reached Switzerland safely.

However, not being competitors, Ernie Smith and Bob Holliday had spent the early hours quietly siphoning petrol from parked German cars into their Ariel Square Four's tank and spare cans, so they overslept and missed the departure. However, when they did reach the market square, they found "SEE YOU UNDER THE CLOCK AT CHARING CROSS" chalked on the pavement. They followed the agreed route and finally caught up with the main party at the border.

En route however, they had all encountered severe storms especially over the Altberg Pass, where for mile after mile they were subjected to very heavy rain along roads that were undergoing almost total reconstruction, so the conditions were very bad indeed. At the height of the storm, Tom Whitton crashed his AJS, ripping open the bottom of its Burman gearbox. The other riders kept him going by stopping every 10 miles or so and dripping engine oil over the gears.

They arrived in Feldkirch on the Austria-Liechtenstein border late in the day with the motorcyclists soaked and very cold. A number of the riders were still in their competition leathers, having left all their other clothes in their hotels in Salzburg. Astonishingly, Harry Perry then went into the town to get a haircut, while Chamberlain visited the local camera shop with a view to buying a German camera before returning home, always having fancied owning a Leica. He didn't buy it though.

George McLean was going round asking after his wife, although Louie McLean had spent the previous week on her own, even staying in a different hotel to her husband... Others took the opportunity to stock up with food and petrol.

The next morning, under somewhat less stressful circumstances, Perks got his BSA Silver Star back off Tozer's trailer, dismantled it and stuffed it into his car again, ready to make directly for Ostende rather than the more busy Channel Ports for which most of the others were heading.

Whitton's damaged AJS took the place of Perks' BSA on the trailer and the large party crossed the border with no trouble at all, presumably because the ONS had warned the officials to expect them. (Oberste Nationale Sporthorde, a politically controlled body displacing the DDAC, Der Deutche Automobil Club, which had performed a similar role to that of our A-CU). They carried on into Switzerland, stopping briefly at St Gallen but then carrying on the further 50 miles to Zurich. The competitors were very tired, but also worried that they could have been seen to have deserted the event rather than, as seemed likely earlier the previous day, possibly winning a number of awards. However, they were merely following instructions and, as it turned out, it was to the same eventual end in any case.

They carried on to France and through widespread preparations for war, being diverted past tank-traps in the road, under mined bridges and through villages being painted with camouflage.

Over the border from Germany and waitng for petrol,
Peter Bradley with Ariel riders Len Heath, Jack White and W.A.West

The roads to Rheims, where they stayed the night at the Hotel Lion d'Or, were choked with military vehicles all along the way, but they got through. Encountering very many others heading for the coast the next day, they nevertheless arrived in Boulogne by late afternoon.

At Rheims, Smith and Holliday had left the party and travelled due west, although avoiding Paris, to return via Dieppe as they had arrived, but being a week early their return tickets were not valid. However, Holliday slipped aboard the ferry and pursuaded the ship's captain that, being "Un pilote de l'Armée de l'Air du Grande Bretagne.." it was essential that he, "..et sa moto, revenent à la suite de toute de l'Angleterre" - or words to that effect. Their machine was prioritised and loaded, whereupon it was insisted they used the captain's day cabin and then drink toasts in cognac with the officers to Les Allies.

The Return Routes Taken by the Main Party

Relevant Channel Ports *are labelled:* **B - Bologne Do - Dover O - Ostend**
Return Routes *are shown as dotted lines.*
Feldkirch *is on the borders of Austria and Liechtenstein.*

The parties split at a number of stages, but the main party stayed in France, continuing to Rheims and so on to Boulogne. Godber-Ford, Gilfinnan, Perks and his passengers left the main party at Nancy, heading north through Luxemburg. Passing the outskirts of Brussels, they went on to Ostend.

127

Chamberlain had wanted to go back through Ostend with Perks, Geoff Godber-Ford and Pat Gilfinnan, as he had enjoyed the casinos in Brussels whilst waiting for Bradley to pick him up on the way out, but nevertheless he did stay with the party and played his part in persuading the Boulogne port authorities to take them and load their vehicles, with Bradley's Delage being the last to be swung on board, despite the long queue being already well established at the port.

So, in less than 48 hours after leaving Salzburg they were back in London.

Earlier however, Godber-Ford on his Sunbeam and Gilfinnan on his Ariel were on their own, having lost touch with Perk's car. Unfortunately they were then stopped and strip-searched between Nancy and Luxembourg, which delayed them considerably, although they were eventually released. They had also been having difficulty finding food and petrol and even around Brussels the petrol stations were all closed, so by about 7pm they were becoming worried. However, riding back out into the countryside they came across a small house with a petrol pump outside. The owner could speak English and explained that he was forbidden to sell petrol until further notice. Fortunately though, he too was a keen motorcyclist and led them around the back of the house where he allowed them to pour about 5 litres of petrol into each tank, refusing to be paid anything so that he could say that he had not sold it.

At Ostend they found Perks and some others, but were told that all places on the ferry were booked, almost entirely by returning English holidaymakers. However, they managed to bribe one of the crew and by 10pm they had their machines on board and were bedding down in the hold for much needed sleep.

They arrived back in England safely, although later than the main party.

So Marjorie had pushed off to start Day 5, as had the Army teams and all the Italians and Germans, which left us pretty much on our own as almost all of the British competitors and spectators had gone, Malcolm and Connor with them. Graham and I just sat at the table, wondering what to do when Lavinda and Peggy came in.

"Peggy! I thought you'd gone with the rest of them this morning?" We were certainly surprised to see her, as the previous night she'd told Marjorie that they were going.

"Oh, er, well, no. You see, Colin didn't want to go, and what with Marjie staying on too, I felt I should stay..." She didn't look very happy about it, but there she was, still with us. And it did make sense, as Colin was doing very well and even if his other team members had pushed off, he was still in the running for an award himself. "And then Lavinda also said that she wasn't leaving early and so..." She looked across at Lavinda for support, and half smiled.

"We'll stick it out, won't we Peggy. It's only a couple more days and then we'll head for home. It'll be all right." Lavinda gave her a little hug and they sat down at our table. "It's not too late for Frühstück is it?" Indeed, it was still quite early and so the hotel was still serving breakfasts, although it was pretty thin, being just bread rolls and cheese, or extremely thinly sliced ham, as usual. There was plenty of tea available though, so we all topped up.

"So what are we going to do today, then? The route looks interesting - it's out north into the mountains of Bavaria and the south of Czechoslovakia and I've never been there - anyone game for it?" Graham was always game for it of course, but Peggy looked less keen.

"We'll be back in plenty of time before they all finish, don't you worry!" he said, but she still wasn't convinced, so Lavinda had a go.

"Oh come on Peggy - you can't just hang around here all day. You'll not hear an English word spoken 'til we return! Look, you can pop onto Roddy's perch and ride behind me." This didn't seem to help at all though.

"Oh Peggy, don't listen to them - you can come with me! Eric can ride his kettle and you can relax in the armchair next to me - what d'you think of that?" I'm afraid that Graham was almost bullying the poor girl, but we didn't really want to leave her there all on her own all day. She looked at Lavinda, who nodded encouragingly, and so she turned back to Graham with "All right - if you're sure you don't mind? I'll be no trouble!" We all laughed at that and so it was decided.

But then it suddenly struck me - what about petrol? The tank of my Scott was just about full as I'd filled it up on the way back on Wednesday and not used it since, but what about Graham's outfit? We hadn't stopped to fill the Squariel's tank on our previous day's ride.

"Not to worry old chap - I've still been queuing up with all the other fellows as usual, filling my tank and then decanting it into a jolly useful milk churn I've found around the back of the hotel. We'll be all right." Well, I'd had no idea what he'd been up to - but it had been a good strategy! Typical Graham.

We met up in our riding gear next to the parc fermé and as we finished checking the machines over, Charles Bennett came across to us.

"What ho - still here I see. Jolly good, jolly good. Off out to see some of the action are you?"

"Well no, actually. We're just going to have a look at something of the countryside north of here. We're too late to get there to see them going out, and we'd be back late if we wanted to see them returning, like we were on Wednesday - nearly missed dinner!"

"Right. Makes sense. Tomorrow's going to be interesting though - can't miss that, what? A bit of racing for a change. Off road, 'scrambling' it's called, and then scorching off along one of their new straight roads - what do they call them? Reichsautobahns I think. Auto-bahn makes sense I suppose, but I'm blowed if I know why everything has to be prefaced with 'Reichs'. I mean, blow it, a 'Mark' is obviously a German coin, so why do they have to call it a 'Reichsmark'? It'll be 'Reichsbrot' and 'Reichsbier' next! Reichsautobahn - that's not the way we do it, is it?"

"No, but then they've built them. We haven't."

"Oh well, we'll just wait and see if they're any good and if so, we'll build better ones! We'd call them 'Fastroads' or 'Mainways' or something. So, any of you chaps tried one yet? We were all escorted along the one into here when we arrived. Very straight they are. Concrete, solid white concrete, straight as a die. Presumably it's because, just like the old Romans, the current German government feels that they can do and go just where they want to, eh?"

We didn't have much to say about that, and as for Saturday's Speed Test, well, I thought we'd just wait and see...

So we finally sorted ourselves out, Graham and Peggy on the Ariel outfit, Lavinda on her Ariel single and me on my Scott. It wasn't such good weather that day, looking rather gloomy over the mountains, but we were heading the other way, due north. We had a good ride that morning, heading out until we came across the Inn Valley that we had met a little further east on the previous Monday. We crossed the river at Braunau, through where the day's route must have passed, but the Kontrolle had been cleared away by then of course and we carried on north, through lovely open countryside. Just after midday we got to Triftern, a small village on the route, and looked for somewhere for a bite to eat.

There seemed to be nothing special there, but we stopped anyway and parked the machines in the Markplatz. However, we soon found a cheerful looking Gasthof on the other side, Zum Hofwirt if I remember it right.

They were indeed very friendly, bringing us great crusty bread rolls, big slabs of cheese and loads of pickled gherkins or something, all to be washed down with their locally brewed beer. Very good it all was too.

We were game for going on further but poor old Peggy was getting a bit twitchy even that early, so we gave in and headed back south again. However, unlike Peggy, Lavinda was feeling perky and she pulled alongside and sort of teased me, before opening her throttle wide and blasting off ahead as we left the tiny village of Voglarn. Well, a thoroughbred steed like a Scott, from a stable that had bred TT winners in its time, wasn't going to stand for that and so we gave chase. Poor old Graham, try as he may with Peggy clenching the sidecar's grab-rail with white knuckles, was left far behind and had to make his way as best he could through all the dust we were throwing up, following the hearty yowl of my Scott's exhaust.

Despite my twin's quarter-litre advantage, Lavinda's Red Hunter led for quite some time, but quality will out, and well before reaching the outskirts of Ulbering we were striding past, with a friendly wave as we did so. She took it in good spirit though and I played the gentleman later on, declining to even hint at the possibility of being able to rub her nose in it.

131

However, when we got back to Salzburg, Bert Perrigo was waiting for us. It seemed that at about the same time as the other telegrams had arrived the previous evening, the recall from the War Office had been misdirected, which is why it hadn't arrived at the same time. It had finally arrived that morning, after everyone had ridden out for the day. So Colonel Bennett had sent Joe Acheson out on his BSA to intercept them while he sorted out the admin and good old Bert waited for everyone to return.

We were the first back and then a rather more serious Colonel Bennett spotted us.

"Ah, here you are. Top whack I'm afraid - we've been called back, maximum priority. I'm waiting for the lads and we'll be off. Get your stuff together, stay on call. Right?" It was the Colonel ordering us around now, not the jolly Charles we'd last been talking to earlier in the day.

Some of the Italian riders arrived back just then, followed by a couple of the Dutch riders with Jaap giving us a wave. Then a Swede came in and some Germans, but there was no sign of our Army teams or of Colin, Alan or Marjorie. We parked our machines and headed back to the hotel rooms to collect our stuff, only to be caught up by Gustav running towards us and calling.

"Eric - you must go! We have had orders to prepare for action, so I fear that things will not be good for you here. Our Colonel Grimm is making, er, Vorbereitungen, ah - plans? We must get you out safely. Schnell! Ja?" He was clearly quite concerned for us, but also stepping out of line I suppose and so he was probably worried that he'd be nabbed.

We assured him that we'd already heard about it and that he shouldn't worry. I squeezed his shoulder and shoved him back to his quarters.

He nodded and hurried back.

132

It wasn't long afterwards that we heard more riders returning and amongst them were some of the Army teams, as well as Colin and Alan too, so we went back out to meet them, Peggy running ahead.

"You all right? Good. But have you heard the news? Oh, right." They'd been told by Joe at one of the controls. "But where's Marjorie?" They didn't know, but we soon did when a German army lorry arrived with Marjorie's Triumph in the back and her in the cab. As she got out we thought it was clear why she wasn't riding because she had two black eyes with a nasty scrape down her cheek and chin!

We helped get her machine unloaded - it wasn't damaged so far as I could see - and joined the group over the way, who were by then all talking and drinking steaming mugs of tea. It seemed that she'd taken a purler earlier in the day but had carried on until she'd been given the message, and that's when a German soldier had offered to bring her back.

And then Colonel Bennett came over, saw Marjorie and gave her a big hug! Well, we'd never have done that, but I suppose that rank has its duty, or privileges. She wasn't put out by any of it - the spill, the big news or the big hug from an Army Colonel - oh no, she just took his arm and said "I suppose we'd better go and see the Korpsführer again hadn't we Charles?" and off they went. It wasn't until a day or so later that she told us what had gone on there.

"Well, we turned up at Hühnlein's office and it seems that he'd caught wind of it already - he was almost in tears I tell you! I suppose it was 'his' event in a way, as he'd been put in charge of organising it after all, so he felt responsible for making it all go smoothly. And for Germany coming out on top of course - but not as a result of everyone else having run away! So he was trying to tell us that it was all a mistake and that we should stay until Saturday evening at least. Charles tried to say his bit, but he couldn't get a word in sideways with poor old Hühnlein telling us that everything would be fine and that he'd got it right from the top - at which point he picked up his 'phone and called Hitler! No, really, he did. Well, he got through immediately and we could hear the Führer shouting down the 'phone from the other side of the room - I don't think he needed a telephone, he could have got through without!" As Marjorie re-lived it, she was clearly still very impressed, if that's the right word for it, but then what happened later and what we eventually found out about it all must have changed our view of it I suppose.

"Seriously, it was uncanny how that man barked it out, just like he was addressing a rally. We didn't need to go, he said. When we did go, on Sunday, we would have an escort to the frontier, with petrol, oil, anything we needed. Yes? Well, basically that's what he said, and being used to being agreed with, and obeyed I suppose, he assumed that was the end of it!" Marjorie paused and looked round, as if wondering if we were still interested? - but she was quite good at telling a story and she certainly had our attention - so she carried on.

"Well no, of course. Good old Charles can speak a little German and so there was briefly almost a three-way conversation going on and he said, as best as I could understand, something to the effect that 'Well Sir, you understand that I'm a soldier and I've had my orders...' So far as I could make out, Hitler's response was just to repeat himself, only louder, to the effect that he gave his assurance that all British subjects would be well looked after and then taken safely to the border. Well, Charles said quietly 'We've had the Führer's assurances before...' and just shook his head at Hühnlein. The poor old chap was so upset when he'd finally put the phone down and sagged into his chair, I felt quite sorry for him."

"Anyway, he pulled himself together and shouted at his secretary to get Colonel Grimm at the double." This was of course the Colonel Grimm that Gustav was watching out for and who, when she finally got round to telling us all about it, we'd also met.

So by the time Marjorie and Colonel Bennett returned, Graham had stowed his milk churn full of ill-gotten gains into his sidecar, together with another 5-litre can he'd found somewhere, and we'd packed all our stuff up and were just about ready to go, but then had to wait for our official escort to get ready. Miss Bunce was comfortably installed in Jack's Bentley, together with her luggage. Alan Sanders and Hugh Sim were there on their Triumphs, while the Army chaps were all lined up and ready too. Their Colonel told a couple of his chaps to put Marjorie's Triumph onto one of the lorries, as she was not riding because of her injuries, to which Marjorie objected, but was overruled. She unloaded her gear and took it with her into Jack's car, not really looking very upset about it actually. Mind you, Jack didn't look too upset either, ending up with two young ladies travelling with him, although the small back seats were not so luxurious for Marjorie and all the luggage.

The Return Routes Taken by the
Army and Remaining Competitors and Spectators

Relevant Channel Ports *are labelled:* **B - Boulogne   D - Dover   C - Calais**
Return Routes *are shown as dotted lines.*
Bregenz *is on the borders of Austria and Switzerland*

The main party stayed together all the way to Calais, with
the exception of Oates who, once back in France, rode west
to Boulogne.   Although only travelling little further south,
Oates passed through different scenes than the others and even
more so for Smith and Holliday, who later recounted that they
had seen large bodies of troops which included Zouaves and
Algerians, with their officers pedalling alongside on pushbikes.

Unlike in Austria and Germany, almost no shortage of
petrol was encountered in France with few obvious signs of
abnormalities in the villages, the farmers being primarily
concerned with gathering in their harvests.   In the towns
however, the expectation of war was more noticeable, with
raw recruits being marched about and commandeered vehicles
being painted in camouflage.   Chamberlain later described it as
"... rather like the gardeners in Alice in Wonderland, all at work
painting the rose trees."

Colonel Grimm appeared, clicked his heels and saluted our Colonel before telling him what was to happen - his English was passable, so what with Bennett's bits of German they communicated quite well. He was tall and slim, very smartly dressed in his Luftwaffe uniform of course. Lavinda later said that she thought he was a particularly good looking chap and not grim at all, but I thought he was rather saturnine and clearly not happy about his latest job. We got to know him a little better over the next couple of days, when he'd relaxed a bit, and I was also pleased to spot Gustav and Otto amongst the men all very smartly lined up behind him, so we'd have their company too.

Unfortunately there were also a couple of Nazi SS types in their black uniforms there too, as well as a particularly unpleasant fellow in a dark suit who didn't seem to socialise with anyone else, but was always poking his nose in. Presumably he was there to keep a watch on us all? They had their own big black Mercedes saloon with a chauffeur, so they didn't really fit in at all, but I doubt that bothered them very much.

Colonel Grimm led off in his great armoured car, with a lorry-load of fully armed soldiers right behind him, followed by us, and then the big black Merc and another German lorry-load, with a couple of big BMW outfits right at the back for good luck. They didn't do things by halves!

So who was in our party then? Well, on two and three wheels there was Graham, Alan, Hugh and Colin, as well as Lavinda and me of course. Then in cars there were Jack, Miss Bunce and Marjorie as I said, while Peggy was in Colonel Bennett's Humber, along with both her's and Colin's baggage. Bert Perrigo was in his BSA saloon, but I think one of the army mechanics was with him, a chap with whom he'd made friends earlier.

The army riders were all on their own machines of course, and that was - let's see, I got to know them all by name in the end. There was Wood, Doyle, Rist, Riley, Dalby, Berry, Mackay, Davies and Smith. Oh, and Joe Acheson, their reserve. Got them all! Not bad, eh?

And then taking up the rear were the two British Army trucks. Well, I say taking up the rear but, like I said, right at the back were the two Wehrmacht outfits, or Gespann as they called them.

So late in the afternoon, with most of the other riders having already done a tough day's riding, we were off. After a few really hot weeks of summer weather it began to cloud over which, together with the failing light, made it all rather interesting. Graham and I were all right, oh and Lavinda too, because we all had good lights, but some of the others were on serious competition machines for which lighting wasn't the highest priority. The German vehicles all had shrouded lights - they were well ahead of the game we later realised - so it was all a bit difficult for us, especially as we didn't really know where we going.

However, we were just following Colonel Grimm's big dark green Horch saloon, while lots more Germans were looking after our tail, so we just hammered on. We soon got onto the autobahn to Munich and as night fell it really was a most weird experience because we could hear the rumble of lots of heavy traffic going the other way, off-stage left, but we couldn't see much of it as they too had shrouded lights or no lights at all. Very strange.

But then it seemed as if the Salzburg Festival had gone for a wider audience and Wagner took to the stage. We could see flashes of lightning far ahead and then suddenly it hit us - a veritable wall of water! It really heaved it down. Now don't forget that Alan and Hugh were still in their competition gear so they must have become totally sodden long before we were. Oh it wasn't particularly cold, just very wet. And then the Donner synchronised with the Blitzen and I was just waiting for one of us to get hit, but it never did, thanks be to the gods up there in Valhalla. What it did do though was to give us brief glimpses of just what was going the other way...

Tanks. There was tank after tank after tank grinding along, all heading east, with big lorries in between, full of dour looking soldiers with the rain pouring off their helmets. As it turned out of course, they were all heading for Poland.

We pushed on in the opposite direction, mile after kilometre, hour after hour, and then at one point we saw brake lights suddenly come on and we all came to a stop. There was one of our army riders, I don't know which one, right over the shoulder of the concrete autobahn. He'd fallen asleep I suppose, but neither he nor his machine seemed to have been too badly damaged - and it had certainly woken him up - so we carried on. I'm afraid it happened twice more - but what could we do? Thankfully everyone survived.

We eventually reached Munich which, even in the dark and after that tremendous thunder storm with the streets just running with water, was really rather impressive and almost romantic I suppose. I wish we'd seen it in daylight and under rather different circumstances, but we didn't get the chance because Colonel Grimm went straight into top gear and threw his weight about, rapidly getting us into a couple of hotels for the night. The one Graham and I were allocated was quite ancient and I'd have liked to taken a closer look around, but in reality we were far too tired to do more than glance at it.

So we got in, dripping all over their floors and feeling really rather embarrassed about it all, but late as it was, they were really very polite and friendly - even feeding and watering us before we gratefully collapsed into our beds.

CHAPTER 12
- in which there is further trouble

"Y'KNOW LAD, there's nothing like being exhausted and dog-tired for getting a good night's sleep. Not that you young 'uns know what it's like to be really tired I expect?" Andy shakes his head, saying nothing.

"So I went in where they told me and - blimey! - I'd got a great big four poster bed all to myself. Never been in one before, or since. I felt lost in the middle of it, I did - but it was cold, oooh, it was so cold - and I was still wet too, I'll never forget that. I tell you, it was a good job I was so tired. I went out like a light the moment my head hit the pillow..." and Eric sighs, as if he's ready for his bed right now.

Saturday 26th August, 1939 **Day 6**

The next morning we were all individually woken by a very polite German soldier rapping on our doors and telling us that we should arise quickly and take breakfast, which we did. However our gear was still wet, unsurprisingly, but we managed to get it on and then oozed downstairs to the dining room - only to find three of the ladies already at table, looking fresh and cheerful. As were our two Colonels, but they were sitting with the SS officers and their Gestapo friend, whoever he was. We were never introduced, so we didn't join them. Lavinda came down just then, looking tidy if nevertheless a little the worse for wear. She chose to sit with us and, while waiting for service, we considered the advantages and disadvantages of motorcycles over saloon cars. Alan and Hugh were still sore about having missed the end of the event though.

"It'll be the High Speed Trial and Scramble today - I wish we were there, don't you Alan?"

"Yes, of course, but if we were still there tomorrow, it could get a bit sticky leaving... But yes, it would have been fun. What did they call it? 'The Cross-Country Speed Test' I think. It was to be along the autobahn, three laps of ten kilometres, they said, and then an off-road scramble. That would be a bit different to just hammering round Donnington Park like we did last year, eh? Mind you, it rained last year too. Ah, but as well as all the water, the autobahn was full of their tanks last night, so I wonder what they're doing about that?" We would never know of course.

We appreciated the hotel's food when it finally arrived - and even the ghastly acorn coffee. Sadly, tea wasn't on the menu, so perhaps Colonel Grimm had chosen the wrong hotel to gather us all together for Frühstück, but of course the reason was so that we could all be briefed for the coming day's adventures. Colonel Bennett stood up, rapped his spoon on the table and told us to pay attention.

"Hope you've all had a good night's sleep, because we've got a fair few miles to cover today!" I remember thinking that he'd probably slept well too, with the difference being that he'd got up with a smart dry uniform waiting for him. Maybe his driver was also his batman?

"Our friends have sorted out fuel for us and Herr Jaeger" - he acknowledged a civilian chap standing at the back - "has sufficient for us at his Shell Depot here." That was a relief - I'd been wondering what we were going to do about that. Mind you, quite typically, Graham had already found out what was going on and so had syphoned the remaining petrol out of his Ariel's tank into his sidecar reservoirs, ready for the now empty tank to be filled later that morning.

"By this time tomorrow we should be in Switzerland. We will be heading south-east to Bregenz today, on the border between Germany and Switzerland, where we expect to spend the night before taking leave of our friends the next morning" and here he included Colonel Grimm and his staff, if not their chaperones. "As I said, it will be hard riding today, as Colonel Grimm tells me that we are going through the Bavarian Forests and up over the Alps. Now, it'll not be as high as you went on Wednesday, but he says we'll be well above the tree line and past a fair bit of snow again it seems. So stay together - we'll set a fair pace, but we'll all need to keep a sharp eye out for what's going on behind us - don't want to lose anyone, what?" and he looked round at us all very intensely. This wasn't just another day's competition with support crews, marshals and rescue waggons all on duty, it was a serious run for home.

It was a pity they didn't all do just as he said though.

We finished our ersartz black coffee and took our gear out to the car park and loaded the vehicles. We were then led to Shell's Munich Depot on the outskirts of the city where we were all filled up to the brim, with Graham enjoying a self-satisfied smile on his face. Thanking Herr Jaeger, we formed up in the order as per the previous day, and set off.

However, unlike the previous day, almost immediately the going was very different and more like the country roads we'd encountered before, especially on Wednesday and Thursday. We did keep up a good pace though, despite the surface soon becoming unmettalled with some sharp chippings scattered about. Fred Rist had a puncture soon on, but it was a treat to watch the army lads go to and fix it pronto. Most efficient they were - I hope the Germans were watching! However, the planned order relaxed after a bit and the Germans who were taking up the rear eventually kept going, trusting us to catch up. Unlike ours, their own military vehicles seemed to be quite impervious to the sharp rocks.

Lavinda pulled over with another flat rear tyre and Colin stopped to give her a hand fixing it again, while up ahead we could see the whole convoy slow down to a crawl until they caught up. I was lucky and didn't get one at all.

The Alps were as beautiful as I had expected, covered in sparkling white snow, but with dark thunder-clouds behind them which added something of an ominous aspect to the scene. The forests were really gloomy and they just seemed to go on and on before we emerged up into the bright sunshine and went over the tops. We were certainly getting a good dose of Germanic grandeur by way of a farewell.

Glancing back over my shoulder, I saw Lavinda way behind me, over at the side of the road yet again. I shut down, checked again and did a U-turn, accelerating back towards her, past the oncoming German outfits.

By the time I reached her, she'd got her bike onto its rear stand and was staring gloomily at the rear wheel. For the third time that day we had a flat tyre in front of us, but now with no more good inner-tubes or patches left at all.

Report Of The 1939 ISDT by von Gustav Mueller

Extract from: *Das Motorrad* *2nd Sept. 1939*

"The disease of punctures started right from the first day on. Pohl from Werningerode had three of them and he was not able to regain the lost time completely within the allowed time. It was a nasty misfortune to lose the Gold medal right at the first day due to just this one piece of ill luck, especially as it remained his only one. For Pohl it had been a small tack the first time, the second time a real carpenter's nail, but riders always help each other. As he had no inner tubes left, he got one from a passing comrade. The other one was in a hurry and unfortunately ripped a tear into his spare tube with the buckle of his belt when pulling it out. Without noticing this mishap, he then he rode away. Poor Pohl stood there with a spare tube with a tear! - but quickly hoisted it as a 'distress flag' and waved it to an oncoming Wehrmacht outfit. The passenger of the outfit threw a spare tube to him without stopping. Of course I don't know to whom this happened, and who the rider of the army outfit was - this might be seen as outside assistance! So as a lesson for those who ride such events: The belt is not the correct place for spare tubes, they should be carried in separate bags."

"By the way, Otto Sensburg, riding a 250 DKW in our Trophy team, also had a puncture the first day. During a previous year's six days trial, after the third puncture he had put the 'evildoer' into his pocket as a talisman and from that moment on he had no further punctures during the whole event. So, this time he also put the talisman into his pocket, but if it did work for him this time, I cannot tell..."

W hat can I do? They seem to have gone..." she said very quietly - and indeed even the dust from the party's passing had settled back down onto the road. It seemed that Lavinda's latest halt had gone unnoticed and we were alone in the high Bavarian countryside, well past the last village, with just a stone hut to be seen further down the road.

"Damn. Sorry, but that's it. Your Hunter's not going any further today. Oh well. But look, you could ride pillion on my bike – Graham's got my stuff in his sidecar so there's room for yours here."

"Pillion? I never ride pillion! That's Roddy's place" and she almost stamped her foot! As is often the case when the magnitude of the situation is too great to deal with, trivia comes to the fore. Brieffly.

"Oh, I'm sorry. Thank you Eric – the knight on the very dusty steed comes to my rescue" - and she gave me a little hug!

So we strained and pushed the Ariel down the road, with its completely flat tyre petulantly resisting progress, along to the hut where I thought we could park it behind and out of sight. However, when we got there we found the door only on the latch and just a pile of old sacks and a couple of shovels inside.

"It's probably a road-menders' hut, but it'll do for us. Just the job – a warm dry stable for your lame horse. C'mon, give me a hand..." and we heaved the 350 through the door.

So with her bags lashed over the Scott's rear mudguard and Lavinda reluctantly perched on the little, hard pillion squab, arms wrapped around my waist, we set off again.

"Where will they have gone? Are we going the right way?" she shouted over my shoulder, but as it turned out there were no options anyway as the road eventually led down into Bregenz and then along the shores of Lake Constance towards the border into Switzerland.

"I suppose they must have gone this way. Not a lot of choice really. Did you hear where they were going to stop tonight? It's getting on a bit." And indeed it was dusk with the sun already having gone down over the magnificent snow-capped mountains west of us.

"No idea. The Colonel said we were going to spend the night in Bregenz, but I don't know quite where he was expecting to stop. Can't be on the Swiss side because the Germans would have turned back at the border - and they've not passed us." She was still shouting, despite us having slowed right down, riding cautiously over the cobbled streets of the small town. "Maybe they are here? Stopped at a hotel or somewhere?"

"Look out for them then!" I'd already been looking around as we pottered slowly through, but hadn't seen any sign of them so far. If they were there, all their cars, lorries and bikes had to be parked somewhere.

No sign of them as we came out of the town either, so we were none the wiser. However, we very soon saw the border posts ahead and slowed as we approached the German Kontrolle. The two young lads in uniform there didn't seem very interested in us, especially when they saw our UK registration number on the front mudguard, and one of them just waved us through. Blimey! I thought - that was easy.

143

The Swiss Border Post was a different matter, however.

We'd been told that there had been a tightening of their controls with the recent influx of Jewish refugees from Germany and Austria, although we'd actually seen nothing of the Nazis' crazy xenophobia in the short time we'd been there. However, we had our British passports and our...

"Oh shit! It's in Graham's sidecar!"

"What? What is?" Lavinda's hand was on my shoulder and she was whispering loudly into my ear. I'd stopped and put my foot down, half way between the two border posts.

"Not my passport, that's here" I said, slapping my breast pocket. "It's my visa – it's with my other papers in my bag that's in Graham's sidecar. And we don't have the letters from the A-CU and the Foreign Office demanding safe passage. The competitors do, but not us. Oh, bugger!"

"Ah. So what'll we do then? But – the others will have already gone through so the guards will know we're with them, surely?" Well, it was worth hoping...

"Look, get your passport out, and your visa – you have got it haven't you? Yes? Good. Well, get that ready too, but not inside the passport." I was whispering too, although the Swiss guard, who was looking at us strangely by this point, probably couldn't hear us over the engine's noise. "If – when - they realise that I don't have a visa, by then you'll have charmed them with your looks and I'll have convinced them that we're not Jews or gypsies - nor secret agents or saboteurs either, but just Brits on holiday. We can but hope." It really did seem a bit thin, but I then looked up ahead. "But if not, just look there – the end of that barrier arm is about shoulder high, so if we duck we could just about get under it and make a run for it. Worth a try if we need to. Just look confident, friendly and cheerful!" I was speaking with far more confidence than I felt, but knocked it into first and eased us forward to the barrier.

"Grüetzi. Ach, Engländer? I too speak English!" and he smiled at us, clearly happy to both show and practice his skills.

"Hello. Er – has there been a large group of British motorcyclists passing through here just recently?"

"Er, 'motorcycles'? Ah, Töff. No, we have no-one today through here." I suppose that's why he seemed so pleased to see us. But where on earth were the others then?

144

"Your passports, please" and we handed them over. He looked at both of them carefully, whilst telling us that he had friends in Oxford - and had seen a Shakespeare play too.

When he asked for our visas, I held out my hand for the passports and to my relief he handed them back, expecting to regain them for stamping afterwards. Lavinda handed her visa over and he looked at it, returning her cheerful smile. He then looked at me, holding his hand out.

"I'm afraid I've lost mine – there was a terrible storm over the passes and the papers completely dissolved in all the water!" Making it up as you go along is sometimes the best way.

"Aaah – nein, das ist nicht guet!" and he frowned, turning to walk back to the office where presumably his superior was waiting. I elbowed Lavinda in the ribs, paddled the bike the extra foot or so to the barrier and ducked around it. Assuming she'd got under too, I opened the throttle.

Her grip around my waist suddenly tightened and I felt her knees squeeze my hips – well, she'd cleared it and was hanging on all right.

I stayed ducked forward and tucked my elbows in. There was a yell from behind us. Leaving it in first gear, I snapped the throttle grip right the way back and hung on. The Scott responded enthusiastically as always, the yowl of its exhaust increasing as we accelerated hard, down and away from the Border Post, swinging right to get behind a big army truck parked there, just in case…

We could no longer hear the guards' yells, but weren't surprised to hear what came next. The sharp cracks from behind us confirmed that there were bullets whizzing overhead.

145

Closing the throttle only slightly and easing the clutch, I snicked it into second and opened wide again. No more bullets so far. We were already up to 45, heading for 60mph and up into top. Thankfully the road was clear, with a reasonably good surface, although Lavinda on the pillion was having to take her weight off the seat by almost standing on the pillion foot-rests - while keeping low at the same time...

"All right?" I shouted over my shoulder.

"Yes. Yes, but won't they follow us?" I eased the throttle a little and we settled down to a slightly more reasonable 50 or so. Looking back, the Border Post was out of sight and there seemed to be no sign of pursuit.

"No, I think it's going to be all right – but keep an eye out behind us..." and I looked down at the engine to check all was in order, which it was, with the big two-stroke twin purring comfortably along. I clicked the oil-pump's supply knob open one more notch.

"Ah, but we're small fry – we're no great threat to them. They were just firing warning shots above our heads - as they'd have to I suppose. And did you see them back at the border post out of Austria? Just a couple of kids and an old chap looking out of the window. Presumably all the real soldiers are away invading Poland, or wherever's next on the Nazi's agenda." I think I was just rabbiting on to relieve my own tension and probably she couldn't hear what I was saying anyway. We carried on at that pace for a few miles, with no lights behind us so eventually I eased off a bit.

"I don't know, but I don't think we need to worry – surely it must have been clear to them that we're not refugees or anything and my excuse for having no visa was quite plausible wasn't it – did you like it? I made it up on the spot!" I was rabbiting again and she was saying nothing. "We'll see. So relax – and let go of my waist a bit, will you?" Lavinda was still quiet – and didn't release her grip on me one little bit.

By then it was getting quite dark – the high mountains in the west meant that night-time came quite suddenly and relatively early, although it was still warm. There was no sign of our party of course and nowhere obvious to stay, so I was getting a little bit concerned – although I'd slept under a hedge before, on more than one occasion. But not with a young lady for whom I then felt a bit responsible, so that when the lights of a cottage appeared up ahead, I slowed down.

CHAPTER 13

- in which good fortune lends a hand

"THEY WERE a friendly bunch, that Swiss family, yes, very friendly. Helpful, they were. Mind you, we thought at first we'd got ourselves into a corner because she hadn't a word of English - not a word."

As Eric sits here in the 21st century, he re-lives not just the events but also the spirit of the times, when any 'civilised' people should be able to speak a little English, surely? After all, most of his pals back at the event had a smattering of English, enough to get by. However, it never crosses his mind that he, an Englishman abroad, could have been at fault?

"Anyway, thank goodness her husband soon turned up."

Saturday 26th August, 1939 **Day 6**

A tall, tidy but somewhat flustered woman had emerged from the farmhouse and, seeing a strange pair of motorcyclists down on the road, she called out to us.

"Grüezi mittenand. Kann ich Ihnen helfen?"

"Oh, hello there!" I replied. "Yes, helfen, help – yes, please, if you can?"

"Was wünschen Sie? Könne Sie Schwitzerdütsch reede?" she asked, but soon realised that she was clearly not getting through, having seen the woman turning to the man and shrugging her shoulders. While many of her words sounded much like the German that we had been hearing throughout the past weeks, it was pronounced differently and with strange words, so I'm afraid that we felt even more at a loss at that point. Waving very briefly at us, she called back into the house "Maa? Maa!" Almost immediately an equally tall, but thinner and slightly older fellow appeared, looking rather surprised.

"Diese Leute sind im Problem. Engländers. Können wir ihnen helfen?" she said to him urgently, telling him that they had visitors seemingly in need of help, while trying to tidy the straying strands of hair and smooth her apron all at once. He calmed her down and took over.

"Es ist gut, Frau. Geh' ins Huus - das Feuer..." and he turned to us - we'd left the bike in the road and were hesitantly walking up to the house.

"Sie sind Englisch, ja? Und your Töff, er, machine - is dead?"

"Hullo," I said, holding out my hand, which the farmer shook in a firm manner. "Ja, we are from England, but nein, our Motorrad ist nicht kaputt. Not this one, anyway..." I replied as best I could, yet again talking too much - still from tension I suppose, but I carried on.

"Er – we seem to have missed our gasthof and need somewhere to, er... Can you help us please?" I'd finally run out of words and Lavinda was no help just then.

"Nei, mir hän wir khui Zemmer zu vermieten. Sorry" he said, shaking his head, but at that moment his wife, who was still standing next to him, said something. "Was? Oh ja, sehr gut." He started to turn back to us and paused. "Ach - nein!" he said, clearly just to himself and then, having worked out the words he wanted, he turned and welcomed us.

"Willkomme. Es ist late, becoming sehr dark. You must come in, meine Ehefrau will bring you, er, food? Ja, food" and he beckoned us into the house with a smile.

I must admit that we were both a bit surprised by this change around, but also by their language as well. It turned out that, while French, Italian and German were spoken in Switzerland, in the north-east where we were it was mostly Swiss-German, or Schwyzerdütsch, so that explained why we could understand some but by no means all of their words. Not that we could understand all of German, come to that! But certainly we were very relieved by their friendliness - and particularly cheered when we got in to see a welcoming log fire at the end of the large kitchen.

We were invited to dispense with our riding gear and settle down at the table, next to two small boys already sitting there, whose eyes were very wide open while their lips were very firmly closed. Lavinda smiled at them and introduced herself and me, but failing to get a response, she just winked at them and gratefully dealt with the thick, dark bread that was being offered by their mother. The man, who introduced himself as Hans, although not introducing his wife, then brought over a large jug of what turned out to be very tasty black Bier which he proceeded to pour for all six of us around the large kitchen table. While I was happy to just enjoy it, and very nice it was too, Lavinda seemed to be sipping rather half heartedly – possibly she was grappling with the concept of very small children drinking very strong beer? However, clearly this was normal and as to be expected, so we got on with the meal - and enjoyed it very much.

As time went on, communications quickly improved as Hans recalled more of his little-used English and we got used to the different way of pronouncing some otherwise partially familiar words. The other three at the table said nothing at all, although they were clearly entranced by what was going on. However, at the end of the meal, clearly signalled by Hans producing his large pipe and a pot of tobacco, she whisked the two boys away, but not before they had formally stood before us.

"Guets Nachtli" they said together, with a little bow, and then ran off giggling between themselves, clearly hardly being able to wait to discuss it all in their bedroom...

We smiled and laughed at this, calling "Gute Nacht" after them.

I thought I'd better share our host's tobacco as he was enthusiastically inviting me to do so, offering me a rather fine white meerschaum pipe which looked rather special and clearly hardly ever having been used. Smoking was a rare thing for me at the time, but I thought that being sociable was a much higher priority just then. Lavinda wasn't included, but then I don't think she ever smoked anyway. Relaxing around the still cluttered table that had fed us so well, we worked at trying to explain our situation, helped later by his wife serving us with what I suppose was locally made Schnapps or something. Who cares – it was good stuff.

I was just getting to the stage of really relaxing when I remembered that I'd left the bike out on the road and so I excused myself and went out to pull it in closer to the house. When I returned with the bags under my arms, it had been successfully explained to Lavinda that, welcome though we were, there were no spare beds or even bedrooms for us, which is just what Hans had said initially. It had soon become clear that we had happened upon a particularly friendly family who were not particularly wealthy, and not often called upon to entertain visitors come to that, relatively remotely located as they were. Nevertheless, there was a dry barn outside and it was a warm summer's evening, so we were welcome to make use of it for the night...

I'll confess that I was briefly lost for words, but soon managed to respond with thanks and a smile, keeping the bags tucked just where they were. I turned to Lavinda, shrugged – and winked.

"We'll make do, eh?" I said and, turning to Hans and his Frau, I attempted a semi-formal bow, with "Dankeschön, und gute Nacht".

"Well, what do you make of all that then?" We were comfortably settled in the barn, having found a good spot and just thrown the bags and then ourselves down into the fresh hay. Comfortable, but it was really rather warm with that hay all around us - it had been a hot day towards the end of a hot summer, so our bedding was acting like an effective storage heater. I did offer her my coat, but it really wasn't needed.

"What a lovely family! But it was just jolly good luck wasn't it? I mean, after my bike getting yet another flat and us losing the group, then being shot at! They did, didn't they? Nobody's ever shot at me before! And ending up all on our own... In Switzerland. I've only ever seen pictures of Switzerland in school books. And here we are - stuck in a barn!"

It had been a very long, tiring and stressful day, with disaster after disaster - and then ending up without even a room to stay for the night, just there in the straw! I suppose it had suddenly all caught up with her.

I heard nothing more from her for a few seconds – and then she caught her breath, and let it all out – sobbing like an abandoned little girl at the end of her unravelled thread. A shoulder to cry on seemed to me to be just so useless, but it was clearly what was needed - and then I realised that she wasn't just being silly at all really, because it was indeed a bit of a nightmare - and perhaps? Perhaps I needed a bit of comforting as well. In fact, damn it all, I needed a hand to hold too, because, bloody hell, at that point all I wanted was to know that I wasn't completely on my own and that it wasn't just me that was suddenly finding that it had all been just a bit too much to take...

CHAPTER 14

WHEN ERIC eventually pauses for breath, Andy finds himself rather lost for words. This isn't quite the grandfather that he thought he'd always known...

"Bit of a lad, then, were you Gramps?" If not finding quite the best words, Andy is nevertheless a bit impressed, although he's reserving judgment as the story is clearly far from over.

"What? Me - 'a lad'? Ah, oh yes, I was one of the lads and I could handle a bike as well as any of them, although I'm not sure about over the really rough bits – that was a different kettle of kippers that was, hammering over those high passes, non-stop all day - it was all I could do to keep hanging on in the sidecar!" Clearly Eric has quite missed what Andy is really referring to - or he's chosen to change direction. "So as for riding a solo on those routes, they were supermen I tell you – and superwomen. Did I tell you about Ruby Slade? Well, Gibbs she was later on, Ruby Bluebell Gibbs. She was a fair trials rider she was, but then her pop was the Norton dealer in Buckinghamshire, George Slade, so she had the best machines for the job right from the start. George was a really good rider and he specialised in the MCC's long distance trials, he did. That's how Ruby got into it, riding a Norton outfit in the Exeter with her pop in the chair. She even won the London Ladies Trial on it! No, but it was solos she liked really. Nortons - she did well on them, and for quite a time after the war too. What's more, the Factory gave her a very special Norton, with elektron crankcases! That's what she'd been riding that week - although I don't know how she'd have got them repaired if she'd ever bashed 'em!" and he smiles to himself as he remembers another character of long ago, while Andy thinks he'll skip it and go and make yet more tea. Or maybe –

"Fancy a coffee for a change, Granddad?"

"Oh no thanks lad, but a nice cuppa tea would go down well. Haven't had a cup of tea since breakfast, and that was a long time ago! Funny how his grandfather can recall even minute details of what he did over seventy years ago, but can't remember the two cups of tea that Andy's already made him this morning.

The new morning dawned bright and clear, as it had for the past month in fact, but for us two straw-covered tousle-headed and still entangled field-mice that were slowly emerging from our nest it was representing something new and wonderful – with hopes of a much better day than the previous one.

"Z'morge? Ah - Frühstück?" We could hear the farmer's wife calling us to breakfast from below, so we hastily brushed ourselves off and dressed, while admittedly somewhat belatedly showing just a little embarrassment the morning after the night before.

Our second meal in our new-found friends' home was a little more frugal, being just a glass of milk, bread rolls and some cheese, but we'd become used to variations on the 'Continental Breakfast' theme by then. We had to be off anyway, but wanted to thank them for their hospitality. I had some Deutsche Reichsmark left, as had Lavinda, but they very strongly refused to accept anything, almost seeming to be insulted by our having offered it. So Lavinda quietly slipped the boys her very last block of Fry's 'Five Boys' chocolate before we all shook hands, made all the right noises and got down to the road.

Just as had we finished lashing the bags onto the machine we heard the sound of motors approaching from the direction of the Border. This could have been very bad news for us – perhaps it was Swiss soldiers finally following up our illegal entry to their country? We thought of getting off the road, but there wasn't enough time to hide the bike, which would have been just a bit of a give-away. It turned out that we had no time anyway because almost immediately a group of motorcycles breasted the ridge and roared towards us.

It was our group of fellow Brits!

The leading bikes drew up next to us, with the rest of them and the following cars and army trucks all piling up behind them in a cloud of dust.

It was at that moment that I realised that we'd been riding on the wrong side of the road the previous night! While Austria had recently been converted to driving on the right, Switzerland continued to drive on the correct side of the road.

"Where the hell have you two been? You missed out on the party! And bloody hell, you really set us up for it back at the Border, didn't you! I mean, blimey, they all…" but at that point Colonel Bennett came rushing up from the Staff Car back at the end of the column.

"Good to see you two – although you've certainly got some explaining to do! No matter now, we've got to get going – got to get to Zurich by nightfall. Right ho, Sargeant, ride on!" and he almost ran back to his car. Lavinda looked at me and almost burst out laughing, but soon regained herself.

"Does he think we're in his army? And what are they on about, 'setting them up'?" I just shrugged at this as I'd already kick-started the bike and had my hand on the gear-lever, but then still found time to reply.

"No idea, but the Colonel's in charge, after all. Rather more importantly though – what was that about a party? I think we missed out!"

"Oh, I don't know…" said Lavinda quietly, as we moved off and joined the column. She briefly turned to look back and waved at the two little boys still watching us from up at the front door.

The roads were clear and in good condition all the way to Zurich. We stopped a couple of times to refill the petrol tanks, have a stretch and a pee, before carrying on. It did give us a chance to get an update though.

"C'mon then, where were you last night?" asked Fred almost as soon as he'd parked his army Beesa next to us. "I mean, we spotted that we'd lost you once we got into Bregenz, but assumed you'd catch us up."

"Oh, we did, we did – but we couldn't find you anywhere in the town and went on through the border into Switzerland, still looking for you. So where were you hiding then?" I felt just a little resentful that they seemed to have made almost no effort to make sure that we could find them again - and then he explained how they'd hidden them.

"Oh we were spread out across the Germania, the Ibis Bregenz and the Kornmarkt hotels and they all had nice big yards behind so we were able to tuck 'em all safely away. But, well yes, perhaps it would have been a bit difficult to spot where we were, come to think of it… But anyway, we soon found out first thing this morning that you'd gone through – crashed through, more like! God they were angry! Got their own back by making us wait, checking everything in triplicate with their guns right up our noses! That's why we were late getting through this morning and why Gordon Bennett is in such a rush. So what on earth did you do?!"

Lavinda was quite happy to let me field all this, in fact she seemed to be rather enjoying it in retrospect.

Anyway, I was explaining it all to an increasing audience until the Colonel came round and hurried us back onto our bikes. Oh – his name wasn't Gordon, by the way, but that's what the soldiers called him behind his back. 'Charles' it was really. Fred Rist had already explained all that to me, but then he was in the Tank Corps, not in the R.A.S.C. like Bennett was, as if it made any difference? I don't know, but anyway he was in charge of the army teams as I said and he did a jolly good job of it really. I briefly met Marjorie and she told me that the Colonel had shoved one of the soldier's machines off the truck so that they could get hers aboard. Certainly her face was still a bit of a mess.

So we all rode on north and into Zurich well before dusk. What a lovely place it was – we suddenly felt like we'd arrived on holiday or something, what with the hotel making us so welcome and Bert Perrigo coming round telling us that the plan was to relax, ready for a long run into France the next day.

So there we were, sitting around nice little tables with the sun slowly setting over the hills, while we sampled some of the rather pleasant French wines. We were relaxing, as ordered.

What's more, the Colonel later told us that the army was going to pay for everything. Well, that doesn't happen very often, does it? But then, they had a budget for the whole trial, with a bit spare for emergencies, which I suppose it was - and for once we were all included, competitors or not.

You know, that still rankles a bit, not feeling included in the main event. I mean, Graham couldn't have competed without a 'passenger' - that was me, in the sidecar. The outfits' crews did every mile together, they were two-man teams. 'Passengers' - humbug! The Germans did it better, calling them 'beifahrer', but nevertheless still only listing the riders as being the competitors, but not the poor suckers in the sidecars. Our names weren't even anywhere in the Programme! As for the TSRs and support crews, well, they certainly weren't acknowledged either. That's why we didn't have copies of the letters from the A-CU and the Foreign Office requiring us to be given help if necessary.

Oh I got over it of course because, on a person to person basis, we were always treated as equals. Well, the Brits did, but don't think poor old Gustav and his pals in the support teams were treated very well, but I didn't hear him complaining, so I don't know really.

The hotel took us in their stride, just dishing out double rooms to whoever was next. Graham had already gone through, so presumably he'd found someone to share a room with, Pat Gilfinnan probably, and then it was our turn at the reception desk. I took the key offered to me and we went to find out where the room was. Neither of us said anything about it, so it was just fine. We let ouselves into the room on the 4th floor and gosh, it was a bit posh, what with us still in our riding gear and filthy boots. We looked at each other, still begrimed with road dirt, standing in the middle of that immaculate white carpet, and we almost collapsed laughing! Her lips tasted of salt and we were both more than ready for a thorough scrub and a de-coke, so I played the gentleman and offered her first go at the bathroom. Now, I suspect that she came from a slightly better background than me, because when she emerged, wrapped in a ginormous towel, she made no comment at all about the facilities - but the lack of a bath and big, powerful shower instead was a bit of a shock for me. Anyway, it was just fine and in a short time I felt rather more civilized. I came out to find her gone, but there was a note left on the table: 'SEE YOU IN THE BAR'

"..and then Otto came back in with another even bigger jug of beer, so we knew it was going to be a good do." For Lavinda's benefit, Alan was re-living the previous night's party, with comments and corrections from Graham and Colin, while Pat and Hugh were over at the bar talking to some of the army types. Anyway, it seemed that Grimm and his men had been rather sorry to see us go, but then we'd all got on very well with them too, although to be fair there were really only one or two that we knew well in the group that had led us out. There was Otto, Gustav and one or two others I suppose, so it's not surprising that the last supper – the farewell party – went well for them all.

"They taught us some of their drinking songs," chipped in Graham. "It was rather late in the evening and I can't remember all the words too well now, but it was very jolly – and loud. God was it loud! And then the Brothers Grimm climbed up on top of a table to give us all a toast: 'Vergesset Auch das Trinken Nicht'. Very good it was too!" Graham would have appreciated it I suppose, speaking a fair bit of German as he did. But he would call Colonel Grimm and his Oberfeldwebel 'The Brothers Grimm', which amused us, if not the Colonel.

"Well yes, that was all quite fun I suppose" chipped in Marjorie, "but dinner, our only real meal of the day, it was just all plates of meat – Fleisch. Don't they like vegetables here? - well, back there anyway – is it all Germany now, or is it still called Austria?" Marjorie looked round for an answer, but we didn't know.

"Anyway, there was just lots of meat and some bread rolls." Marjorie made a face at the thought of it, while some of the others just shrugged and Alan muttered something about it being good food.

"The bread was fresh, but they brought us just a few tiny rolls of butter with it - I mean, gosh, we'd ridden hard all day and all we got was lots of meat, bread and a miserly portion of butter! Fortunately our friend the Colonel looked after us and shouted at the staff so we soon got voluminous quantities of butter - together with a great pile of boiled eggs and jam too!" Marjie had laughed at the memory of it.

"And then we had coffee served. Well, they called it Kaffee, but it was just made out of acorns again. It was ghastly. Worse than the last time! But then you asked for a second cup, didn't you Alan? I thought you must be joking, but Colonel Grimm took you seriously and called the hotel proprietor, demanding a second cup of their Kaffee for us all! Well really, I didn't want another one – I hadn't finished the first one!"

156

It seemed that coffee and other things were rationed, so they must have been being treated very well I suppose. This was before we had any rationing in England y'know, so it was all a bit strange for us at the time. She told us that Colonel Grimm had to provide the hotelier with written authority to supply anything extra! Mind you, they also told us that yet again he'd paid for the whole thing. Hotels, food, drink - everything. Amazing really. So, despite the rotten coffee, it sounded like they'd had a good party and Graham finished off the tale for us.

"They knew how to have a good time did those chaps and then, round about one in the morning I think it was, they wound it all up and got together, all in order, lined up, to sing us a lullaby. Well, it was Brahms' 'Guten Abend, gute Nacht' and they sang it well, I do say. In parts, no less!"

Personally, looking back on it, I think that Lavinda and I had a better time with our Swiss family in their little farmhouse with good, simple food, beer and tobacco. Yes, we did all right really. Not that we told our pals about it, but then they didn't ask.

Graham told us that the next morning in Bregenz had been run on army terms, with an early start, a quick bread and cheese breakfast, with some of the eggs left over from the night before, and then all lining up at attention by their bikes. I'm glad we weren't there! There were lots of good-byes all round, I'm sure. They told us that Colonel Bennett of our Army formally shook hands with Colonel Grimm of their Luftwaffe, then stepping back and saluting.

I can certainly see that's just how they would indeed have done it – but it turned out that, while it seemed to be simply friends saying goodbye, only one week later they were to be enemies...

Meanwhile, I'm afraid that our dash through the Swiss Border Post the night before really had then caused difficulties for them, as Fred had already told us. However, unlike us, they had all the correct paperwork, with official letters from the government and all, so they got through, eventually.

They had lost a lot of time though, so that's why they were pushing it a bit when they then met us just over the border in Switzerland, as I've already said.

Almost as soon as their account of what we had missed the night before was finished, we were called in for dinner in the hotel's restaurant, so we topped up our glasses and wandered in. It just carried on reinforcing the image of being on holiday! Tables all laid out, with fresh linen, napkins, polished silverware and with waiters standing in line ready to place the chairs for the ladies and take our orders. What a contrast, even with our good digs back in Salzburg.

Lavinda and I were pleased to find ourselves sitting next to Bert over dinner. He was BSA's Competition Manager and he explained that, as there were some very special Beesas being used by the army teams, he'd been there to look after them. Not that they needed much looking after as they all went very well throughout the trial and throughout our dash home too.

He was very good company, cheerful and with so many amusing stories that the evening just flew past. Oh, and the food was good too, although I can't really remember what it was now, but I do know that we had four courses and we ate the lot! Even Marjorie didn't complain about it. Then, towards the end, over the real coffee - and there was plenty of it too - Colonel Bennett stood up and thanked the manager and staff, which I thought was a nice touch, and then reminded us that we had an early start for a long ride the next morning.

We didn't need any encouragement to turn in after a long hard day's riding, followed by a few drinks and a good meal, and so Lavinda and I were probably among the first to head off, knowing that the next day would bring yet more tough going.

I don't remember much after that, but we certainly slept well.

CHAPTER 15

ANDY HAS just about come to terms with his grandfather's past by now and he leans over and gives Eric's shoulders a hug. But then he thinks it all over - and really, it actually sounds almost unbelievable...

"So there you were, just a week away from being at war with Germany, and you're partying with them, right on their territory - and at their expense too? That's cool!" and he laughs at the mere thought of it.

"Well, no - because we missed out on that last supper with the Brothers Grimm. Didn't I explain that? You see..." but Andy cuts him short.

"Yeah yea, you explained all that, but the squaddies - they were with the Germans, weren't they? All pals sharing drinks and things? Were they really pals?"

"Oh yes, most of us were - we'd met in previous years, at the ISDTs and at other events too I expect. They were only in it for the motorcycling you know - well most of them. I remember Otto telling me one night, late it was and we'd had a few bevvies y'know, and he got going on about how much he hated the uniforms and all the saluting and, well, everything really. He was a good chap was Otto, but he'd have got it in the neck if they heard him talking like that y'know. I wonder what happened to him?"

"Well yeah, but even better, before that you said that there'd been British Army lorries, cars and 'bikes all running along the autobahn, all in jolly company with the Wehrmacht! I'm glad I believe you Granddad!"

"Believe me? You've got to believe me! Do you think I'm making it all up? Well I don't know, the youngsters of today, they don't respect their elders. It's not like when I was a lad!" and he's waving his arms about and beginning to go red in the face...

"Gramps, Gramps - of course I believe you. It's an amazing tale you're telling me, and no, I don't think you're making it up. Calm down, relax!"

"Now come on - what happened next?"

159

Monday 28th August, 1939

Well, the next morning we were all called horribly early - woken up by sharp knocking on our door. I don't know quite what time it was, but for us it was a bit of a job getting going, I do remember. Anyway, Lavinda went off for another shower or something while I got down to check the bike over. It was fine - I'd stopped the oil pump back down again and it had been running clean, with plenty of oil left in the tank. I gave the chains a lick of oil while a couple of soldiers came round with the jerry cans of petrol. I'd also got all my papers out of Graham's chair, but left the bag there for the time being, along with Lavinda's, making less load for the Scott, you see.

Then it was back into the hotel's restaurant for breakfast - and it was just a bit better than the frugal excuses for breakfast we'd been offered previously!

We were just finishing when Graham came over to us and offered Lavinda a ride in his sidecar. Now, by this time he'd just about emptied his milk churn of petrol and dumped it, transferring what was left into his nicked 5-litre can, so there was room for her. But to my surprise - and delight - she chose to carry on riding with me! Graham shrugged, smiled, winked at me and pushed off. I felt like top dog, I can tell you.

Well, we rode on and got to the border of France by about midday Monday, but this time we were with the Army, so there was no problem for us getting through that time.

160

We crossed over at Versul, got everything stamped and then Colonel Bennett came across to tell us that he had gained permission for us to use the military road along the Maginot Line. That wasn't the shortest distance to the Channel, but it meant that we would have a good road all the way, with hopefully no obstructions as it was closed to all civilian traffic.

Traffic. Well, that was interesting in itself I can tell you. There were military vehicles all over the place - preparing for war as it turned out of course. France had, it seemed, been mobilised and so the Line was teeming with hundreds of French soldiers, we could see that - but much good it did them in the end. I mean, even then we were laughing at it. Oh yes, the Maginot Line was really very impressive, with as much underground as there was above, with tunnels, telegraph lines - and even a railway along one stretch! They didn't show us around of course, but the Colonel was telling us about it later that evening. He said that building it had already almost bankrupted the French government, and they hadn't finished it yet! However, what we wanted to know was, should it ever come to that, why wouldn't the Germans just fly over it or drive their tanks around the ends? The recent Spanish war had already shown what the Germans could do from the air... The Colonel just shrugged and made no comment.

Anyway, thankfully all those soldiers and their vehicles didn't get in our way and we made good progress along their nice new military road, heading north-west towards Belgium.

As I said, we were keeping up a good pace and making good time - until we got to Belgium late that afternoon. We didn't actually need to go through Belgium, but that's the way the Colonel led us and so we came to the Belgian border post.

Well, they didn't like the look of us! Oh no, not at all. They weren't friendly guards in front of us, I can tell you. But then, I mean, it must have looked a bit suspicious really, a dozen or so bikes, most of them ridden by unarmed soldiers, followed by two army trucks with no weapons anywhere, a staff-car and two civilian cars, all boldly arriving together in broad daylight with their paperwork perfectly correct - clearly we were ne'er-do-wells... No, really, we were arrested on the grounds of being German spies!

We were all marched off to the Town Hall and brought before their Lord Mayor - who thought it was very funny and told us to go away, or words to that effect. Well, by then it was getting dark and so it was decided that we would stay overnight in this lovely friendly Belgian border town.

The Colonel went back to talk to the Mayor, who eventually gave in and sent an underling round to sort out overnight accommodation for us all. The army paid for it again, thank goodness. I'm not sure how they did it though. All I had were some left-over Marks, a thin wad of pound notes and a fiver - nothing Belgian - but the army sorted it out somehow. It even included a couple of rounds of Belgian beer for each of us, so it wasn't so bad. That's when we were nattering with the Colonel, and off duty he really was good company. As I said, he was telling us about the Maginot Line that we'd ridden the length of that day, so that, together with a nice couple of cold beers, it was good way to relax after a hard day's riding. Then it was time for supper.

Given that we'd just turned up out of the blue, they did very well for us really. I mean, the locals were just like anyone anywhere else. After all, you don't say no to a bit of unexpected trade and they treated us well enough. Friendly they were and had good real coffee for us too - and even plenty of tea! I wasn't so keen on their hard bread and sausages though - and poor old Marjorie must surely have lost a fair bit of weight that week!

I've no idea about Marjie really of course, but I was learning a bit about Lavinda and we got on ever so well. Somehow we never ran out of things to talk about and I seem to remember there was a lot of laughing and smiling and things. Oh, she'd told me about her friend Roddy, who sounded a bit wet to me, but she seemed to like him, and so in turn I must have told her about Emily. But well, we were a long way from home, in rather unusual circumstances - bloody dangerous really! - and, well, for a short time it took our minds off it all I suppose...

Just like the previous morning, we gave the machines a check over before going back in for breakfast. My trusty Scott was doing well, but the rear tyre was looking a bit thin! I adjusted all three chains, although the magneto's was fine really. I needed a refill of engine oil and of course the army lads had no specialist two-stroke oil, so I made do with ordinary straight 40SAE and it was just fine.

Makes you wonder if it's really worth paying for the special 2-stroke stuff, but probably it makes the sparking plugs last longer? Oh, I cleaned them too. I adjusted the clutch cable a bit and tightened the fork damper - we'd been bouncing a bit over the Belgian pavé and I hoped that would help, but it didn't. Surprisingly the radiator didn't need topping up, despite the very warm weather, but then, while we'd been keeping up a good pace as I've said, we weren't really hammering it and there was a good air-flow, so it had coped very well.

Apart from filling the petrol tank, that was about it so we went back in to fill ourselves. Well, not 'fill' - it was back to just bread and a bit of cheese once more, but we got down what we could and togged ourselves up ready to go.

"Right-ho chaps, it's hopefully the last stretch before we ship back over to Blighty. Take it easy - it would be damnable to have a nasty this side of the channel, eh? Lieutenant Riley - you take the lead again - steady but don't hang about. Keep it tight, chaps - show 'em we know how to do it!" and Colonel Bennett strode back to his staff car, which now also had Marjorie and Miss Bunce comfortably ensconced in the luxurious back seats because Jack had peeled off to get back to Cologne. Marjorie's cheek and chin were by then much better, although still well bruised, but she had more sense than to insist on getting back onto her bike when there was a nice big comfortable Humber to ride in!

We rode through Belgium and then back down into France. The French didn't think we were German or even Belgian spies and let us in with no problems. At that point Graham left us too - he was heading south for Boulogne while we were crossing from Calais. So I retrieved our bags and one of the soldiers topped his tank up for him while the girls gave him a hug and kiss on the cheek. A fair bit of hand-shaking then went on before he came over to me to say goodbye.

"Thanks for all your help Eric. You made a good charioteer and we'd have done really well if it wasn't for that blasted magneto... Oh no, it was the pilot jet wasn't it, on the second day? Anyway, I'll go for you again and we'll get it right next time - yes? Right, cheerio chap, take care, and I'll see you in a week or so. Keep in touch."

We didn't of course, but how were we to know? We never did ride together again and sadly we've lost touch since. I must say it was rather strange for us to see him ride off all on his own, just as he'd arrived, the distinctive purr of his Squariel still being heard even after he'd swung round the bend and out of sight.

Oates travelled south across France at a good pace and with no problems, but was then flagged down just outside Boulogne by a well dressed couple standing by a Rolls-Royce at the side of the road. They explained that they had run out of petrol en-route to the port. At this stage, with not far to go and not yet on reserve, Oates still had his spare can full of petrol in the sidecar, so he replenished their car's tank.

They continued to Boulogne and after a wait on the shore they managed to get onto the next ferry, which was a stroke of luck in itself. Naturally the three of them stayed together during the crossing, whereupon Oates learned that his new friends were no less than Hollywood film director Alexander Korda and his newly wed wife, the film star Merle Oberon. They had been on their honeymoon when news of the troubles had reached them and they had cut short their post-nuptial vacation and headed for the Channel. Oates had greatly enjoyed one of Korda's recent films, 'Rembrandt', which had starred Charles Laughton, and so they were not short of things to talk about during the short voyage.

The RAC were in charge of the evacuation and the embarkation and were naturally concerned with maximising the passage of people, but not necessarily their vehicles. Consequently, both the Ariel and the Rolls-Royce were left on the French quayside. For some reason, Korda didn't seem particularly concerned about this, but Oates' machine belonged to Ariel Motors and he was worried about the repercussions of his not being able to return it.

From then on, for us and our army convoy heading towards Calais, it got a lot worse. The roads were clogged with military traffic, mainly heading east, with giant trucks and tanks completely dominating the roads.

As we got closer to Calais the roads were littered with abandoned British cars! Oh, and even earlier we'd passed a Roller stuck at the side of the road. There seemed to be quite a lot of posh cars around when we were there, but I suppose back then it was usually only the wealthy types who could afford a continental holiday - unless you were doing it on the cheap like us of course. This one was a two-seater coupe and very nice it looked too, although the bonnet was up and it wasn't going anywhere. It had probably run out of petrol, because as we all know, a Rolls-Royce doesn't break down. However, there were plenty of people trying to help, and we hadn't got petrol to spare anyway, so we all just passed on by.

With hindsight, this must have been just about three days or so before Germany invaded Poland, but the writing was clearly on the wall you know, so word of the impending conflict had spread to most of the Brits on the Continent, either on business or holiday, and, like us, they were heading for the safety of home. I suppose we must have been just about the only British military party travelling in France that day!

However, unlike us who'd been well stocked up with petrol by our German friends, many of them had completely run out of fuel, so they had abandoned their cars and got to the port as best they could. We saw all sorts at the side of the road. There were Lagondas, Rileys, Fords - everything from Austin 7s to Bentleys. At the port we even saw a nearly new Talbot saloon that had been abandoned. Not many motorcycles left lying about though.

As you'd expect, our Colonel got directly in touch with the people in charge and explained that he had a small convoy of military vehicles that had priority for getting back to England. He was told that the best they could do would be the first ferry leaving the following morning – nothing could be done before that. And yet again we civvies were thankfully lumped in with the army types. He came back and explained the situation to us, so we parked all the vehicles tightly together and the Sergeant organised a guard rota through to the morning. We were much comforted by that as the docks were just heaving with people, both British civilians wanting to get away soon and French soldiers wanting to do something, anything, immediately, and so consequently they were all feeling increasingly frustrated and short tempered...

As a result of not being able to get away until the next day, we had the rest of the day and all night to kill, so we left the Scott tucked in with the rest of the parked and guarded convoy and went away from the noisy crowded docks to have a look around. Alan and Marjorie joined us and we soon got away and up into the old town. I think we were probably looking for a place for a drink or a bite or two, but pretty soon we realised that things were too far from normal to be able to expect to just sit under a shade on the pavement with a nice drink and watch the world go by. Oh no, all hell was going on, with the town blacked-out and soldiers everywhere. Well, I say soldiers, but most of them were recently recalled conscripts who'd had trouble finding all of their uniforms in time, so they were pretty ragged and some even had patched army trousers that had been used on the farm – certainly their boots had seen a lot of pig-shit in the recent past. I tell you, it almost made an effective camouflage! In different circumstances it would have all been very funny, but there were so many of them, mostly disorganised and looking so worried that it wasn't funny at all.

As you can imagine, gangs of worried young men who had recently been given guns and a small amount of ammunition were not to be messed with on their own patch. Oh, there were nevertheless some organised activities to be found and we came across an officer distributing cans of petrol and sending off pairs of soldiers to commandeer some of the abandoned vehicles outside the town – I bet their owners never saw their precious cars again.

Eventually we did find somewhere for a drink and something to eat and then, as night was drawing in, we headed back for the docks. When we got there we were stopped by a sentry at the entrance.

"Arrêt! Qui va là? Ami ou ennemi?" I'm sorry, but it was all we could do to stop bursting out laughing, although Alan did reply "Enemy!" which didn't help at all. The sentry must have been no more than fifteen or sixteen years old, with patched trousers and old brown boots, but an immaculate bright red tunic with polished buttons – and the bayonet on the end of his rifle was a piece of silver-painted wood.

"My God – our gallant allies, protecting us from across the Channel! What chance is there?" Marjorie was sort of joking, but it turned out not to be a joke at all in the end of course. Anyway, we persuaded him to let us through without prodding us with his bayonet and we went back to the vehicles.

There was no news – just wait 'til morning - so Lavinda and I looked for somewhere to kip. Now, by that stage we clearly knew that this time there was no point in hoping for a comfortable hotel room or anything, or even a wash and a bed, so we were just looking for somewhere dry, out of the breeze, and preferably quiet with a little bit of privacy.

We also both knew how it was and how it would be for us. That it was probably going to be our last night before we returned to reality, normality – and our own partners. It was far from ideal, but we made of it what we could.

167

Despite all the promises, we weren't first aboard the morning ferry after all because the dockers just gave in and let on those at the front of the clamouring queue - and it was a long queue, with some of them having been waiting for days. So no, we didn't get on and had to wait for the next boat which arrived just before midday. Even then, our collection of dirty motorcycles, a couple of disreputable looking army trucks, two grubby cars and load of exceedingly grimy motorcyclists all getting on board in front of the magnificent Rollers and their wealthy owners didn't go down too well at all. They had to just stand by and watch. It was terrible and our hearts bled for them.

By way of something of a contrast to what had gone before, the trip back across the Channel was quite quick and smooth, with a calm sea and no problems. So there we were, on the last significant leg of our long run home, just relaxing and letting someone else do the driving. Well, maybe not actually succeeding to relax, as we were probably all still fairly wound up, but the light at the end of the tunnel was by then shining brightly for us. Well, for most of us anyway. Lavinda and I mainly sat at the stern, just holding hands. We didn't say much for once. There wasn't much to say really.

We got to Dover and they unloaded our vehicles first, so there wasn't much waiting around, not like on the way out! Sometimes it helps to have friends in uniform pulling rank. So then the only thing left was for us to say goodbye to all our army friends, get back onto the Scott and bumble the mile or so to Dover Priory Station for Lavinda to get home by train. The day's surprising lack of problems and good timing kept going and, as we parked and she jumped off, the Station Master was blowing his whistle and waving his flag. So, ignoring the ticket office, Lavinda was able to hop on just in time. I was checking that the bike wasn't going to slip over on the gravel but, as I turned back, the train was moving away and so I just glimpsed her waving through the window.

And, before you ask, no, I never saw her again.

CHAPTER 16

- in which a few loose ends are tied up

ANDY WONDERS if his grandfather will continue, but Eric has closed his eyes, while his chair carries on gently rocking...

The plates and cups need dealing with and so Andy quietly tidies them away.

As far as can be ascertained, every single one of the British competitors, crew, supporters and spectators at the 1939 ISDT managed to return safely. Many of the riders were to survive the coming war and successfully resume motor sport again afterwards. Sadly, far fewer of their German fellow competitors are known to have done so.

Something of what then happened to just a very few of the many competitors in that memorable event is recorded here, but there are certainly many more tales yet to be told.

Graham Oates waited at Dover in the hope of retrieving the Ariel and was greatly relieved when the next morning's cargo boat unloaded the outfit. He rode it home to Liverpool, although it turned out that Ariels were in no hurry to have their machine returned after all, being flat out making singles, both W/VAs and W/NGs, for the British and French governments.

Soon afterwards, Oates' garage in Liverpool was totally destroyed by a direct hit during a German air raid aimed at the Liverpool Docks, so Ariel Motors never did have their 4H and Noxal sidecar returned. Sadly, the air raid also ended his business, 'Graham Oates Motors'. It had been the last ISDT in which he competed.

Graham Oates
in the
1936 ISDT

Ariel RH500

Oates joined the Royal Army Service Corps as a motorcycle instructor, having been a despatch rider himself on a Triumph Model H in WWI. In due course he was to experience riding most of the British machines used in WWII, including Ariel W/NG, Norton WD16H, BSA WM20 and Matchless G3/WO. He was promoted to Major and then to Colonel in the 9th Training Battalion, R.A.S.C.

When the war ended, he was posted to Germany as Head of 'Roads and Road Transport', helping re-establish communications in the chaos following the collapse of the Third Reich. He organised the British Army teams for the ISDT and also Germany's first post-war motor race in Stadt Park in Hamburg in 1948, at which Ferdinand Porsche raced his prototype sports car. Oates was also involved in the re-commissioning of the VW factory and himself bought the second Beetle off the line, taking it back to the IoM with him.

He was still involved with motorcycling until the late '60s, involving the Manx Two Day Trial for which he donated the '*J. Graham Oates Trophy*' for the sidecar class, which is still being awarded. He was a founder member of the IoM Branch of the VMCC. He died in 1972.

Geoff Godber-Ford, having arrived in Ramsgate, was still asleep until one of the crew shook him awake. To his surprise, Pat Gilfinnan and the others had already gone. He rode home in some pain as his throat was extremely sore and it turned out that breathing in dust over the past week or more had caused ulcers in his throat. His doctor cut them out on the spot, an experience he remembered long afterwards.

Despite already being a very successful international trials rider, an earlier accident in a Morgan three-wheeler, which severely damaged his knee, prevented him from any wartime active service and so he started a bakery business supplying the NAAFI.

Moving to Somerset after the war, he once more competed in MCC events as he had done before the war, including the Exeter, Land's End and Edinburgh Trials. He was also a works rider for Nortons, riding a 500T with considerable success until Nortons finally withdrew from trials in the 1950s. He was then offered a Douglas by the works, but he couldn't get on with the flat-twin and only rode it in two events. Then came a 197cc Villiers-engined B2C Norman, soon followed by a Dot which he did like, competing in many trials on it, including the Scottish Six Days Trial. He retired from competition in 1956. He was still enjoying riding into his late 80s, once more back on bicycles, including a Moulton, followed by a recumbent tricycle of his own design.

Fred Rist represented the Army in both the 1938 and '39 ISDTs, having joined the Royal Tank Corps in 1934 and training as a trials rider at Farnborough.

During the war he was in the Western Desert where he enjoyed 'testing' captured BMW and Benelli motorcycles, possibly preparing him for his post-war sand racing at Pendine Sands.

He was then in the 1947 BSA team, successfully competing in trials and then grass and sand track, hill climbs and road racing. A true clubman, he always rode his machine to and from the events, with a straight pipe in his haversack to replace the road-going silencer.

His last ISDT was in 1952 when he personally gained a Gold medal, while his team, riding BSA A7 Star Twins for the Birmingham MCC, also won the Team Award. This was followed later that same year by a fast 3,000-mile European tour which gained the Maudes Trophy for BSA.

Successful 1952 BSA Team for both ISDT and Maudes Trophies
Brian Martin   Fred Rist   Norman Vanhouse   Team Manager Bert Perrigo

When he retired from competition, Rist moved to Neath in S.Wales to run a BSA dealership. He died in 1995.

Marjorie Cottle was riding a factory entered 250cc Triumph Tiger 70 in 1939, competing for both the Hühnlein and Bowmaker Trophies along with Godber-Ford and Sanders. However, she was already well known for successfully riding in the Raleigh Works Team with style, competing in many national events and ISDTs.

Marjorie Cottle
and
Miriam Anning

1928 ISDT
at Harrogate

Furthermore, she had covered over 3,000 miles in the 'Raleigh Round The Coast Ride' obtaining wide publicity for both the firm and herself. The fact that she was riding in Germany that summer, but was late in returning, meant that she was back in the news again.

Consequently, as soon as she arrived back in England she was persuaded to take part in the television version of 'In Town Tonight', the well established BBC radio programme in which people who were in London at the time were interviewed on topics of current interest. Cottle described the preparation beforehand at BBC Alexandra Palace.

"It was all quite interesting - they put some ghastly yellow paint on me which made me the most weird colour! They did my hair and made such a fuss of me, before taking me in front of the camera to be interviewed."

They asked her about her adventures and she told the viewers what it was really like over in Germany and France at that time, which by then was just a couple of days before war broke out.

174

However, the threat posed by Nazi Germany had been evident and plans for the possible closure of BBC's TV service were already in place. The reasons were that, with resources likely to be at full stretch fighting a war, television for only around 20,000 viewing families in London and the Home Counties was a luxury the nation would not be able to afford. Also the single transmitter at Alexandra Palace would serve as a direction-finder if enemy aircraft approached London.

"I actually got in on the last night of television broadcasting before war broke out. The very next day they closed it down and that was it until the end of the war." (On Friday 1st September 1939, at around 12.15pm, the service came to an abrupt halt. After the final edition of the Remote Outside Broadcast from Radiolympia 'Come And Be Televised', and then a Disney cartoon, the transmitter was switched off.) "So I finished it all with a little bit of a flourish!"

Indeed, given that television was only broadcast for just a couple of hours each day during the three years before the war, to appear on it would have been something really rather special.

Marjorie carried on riding after the war and her last motorcycle ride was in 1980 on the Isle of Man when she rode a Gilera, sans gloves or helmet, but with a big grin.

She died in 1987.

Fred Perks had competed in three ISDTs and gained a Gold in 1937, crashing in '38 and then retiring with a clean sheet in '39. He made it home safely from Ostend, only to find his call-up papers waiting for him.

He enrolled as a Despatch Rider, arriving for active service at the local drill hall in the early hours of the morning, with his freshly cleaned and serviced BSA M23 Silver Star ready for action. Astonishingly, there he was told that civilian machines would not be needed and that he should take it away.

Upon being eventually sent with other DRs to Chilwell to be issued with their WD machines, he found that they were mostly civilian machines and they were given tins of green paint and brushes and told to camouflage them. There was at least one BSA 350 Trials bike with a chromium plated tank, while Perks was issued with a new BSA M23 Silver Star...

A week later, Perks was back in France, although the M23 pinked badly on the Army issued petrol. (Similarly, Fred Whitehouse had also been issued a BSA Gold Star for DR duties in France.)

However, by the end of the year, Perks' M23 had been written off by a lorry and he had been issued with a side-valve BSA M20, which ran well on the low octane petrol. He later said "I was happy with the M20 – it was a good slogger and reliable for the job."

When France fell in 1940, he got out through Marseilles and eventually returned home a very long way round, via Gibraltar and then Newfoundland.

Perks survived the war and continued motorcycling for many years afterwards.

Jaap Fijma had won the Dutch Championship at the Assen TT in 1934, riding a 250cc Grindley Peerless. He competed again in '35 on a 500cc Velo, in '37 & '38 on a 500cc Ariel and in '39 on a 500cc Velo again, when he came 6th. Meanwhile he had ridden successfully in the Dumonceau Reliability Tests as well grass track racing. He represented his country in both the 1937 and '39 ISDTs, riding a 500cc Ariel.

Surviving the war, he continued competing in a wide range of events while also running a motorcycle shop in Amsterdam with his business partner van Oosten.

He died in 1969.

After his active career in racing, he was a Technical Judge for the Assen-TT Organisation, as seen here in 1961.

Otto Sensburg had competed in ISDTs since 1934, mostly riding DKWs, and by the end of his career had collected no less than 8 Gold medals!

Surviving the war, he rode a 244cc DKW for the German Trophy team in the 1954 ISDT and then drove a DKW L3 Sonderklasse 2-stroke in the Mille Miglia, with Willy Brandt as co-driver. Then in 1956 he was the Team Manager for the German ISDT teams, although the event was tarnished for them by one of their rider's interference with the Scrutineers' marker tags, with Sensburg very strongly criticising such behaviour.

He was the DKW main dealer in Munich until the end of production in 1966.

Ludwig (Wiggerl) Kraus started early, being apprenticed with BMW at the age of 14. By 1929 he was in the sidecar of a very successful BMW outfit and then won his first hill climb in 1931. By then he was already known as 'Wiggerl', competing in the ISDT from 1933 to '35.

In 1936 he was road racing as a BMW Works rider, becoming the German Champion in 1939 upon winning at Nurburgring in the 500 cc solo class. In both 1938 and '39 he won the Bukarest GP, then riding a 596cc BMW outfit for the German Trophy team in the 1939 ISDT.

After the war he continued as a private entry in both the solo and sidecar classes together with his sidecar passenger Bernhard Huser. Riding solo, he was Vice Champion in the 500cc class on BMW in both 1948 and '49, behind Georg Meier. From 1950 on, Kraus & Huser were the official BMW works team, and after many wins became German Sidecar Champions. This was repeated in 1953, when they also rode a 600cc BMW outfit in the ISDT.

Kraus almost always used the start number 56, which was emblazoned on the distinctive white pullovers worn over his and Huser's leathers.

He died in 1987.

o ———————— o

Further information about those involved in the 1939 ISDT would be welcomed, with the possibility of inclusion and acknowledgment in future publication.

AUTHOR'S NOTES
- writing this book has not turned out as expected

Having long ago discovered the basics of a great story, but with a seemingly very small number of facts available, I thought the door would be open for me to let my imagination run free and fill in all the big gaps to make a great adventure story. However, the longer I looked, the more I found. So much so in fact that it eventually became clear to me that there was already enough for it to be a reasonably full factual account in its own right. But I didn't want to write yet another 'text book'.

Introducing Eric is merely a device to connect all the stories together, while taking the opportunity to explain some of the context to the reader, aka his grandson, Andy.

As briefly mentioned in the story, there are no official records of the names of the sidecar 'passengers' (although they were and still are far more than mere passengers) or of the reserve riders, support crews and TSRs, or indeed any of the many others that were formally involved in the 1939 ISDT. Nevertheless some of their names can be found, mainly in the subsequent accounts by competitors and officials and so those have been incorporated, as and where appropriate. However, there is no trace to be found of the name of the unknown occupant of Graham Oates' Noxal sidecar, even in Oates' otherwise very useful biography, but he must have existed and I have called him Eric Dale.

Consequently, while it was certainly interesting to write and, hopefully worth doing, it turned out to be far from the no-holds-barred piece of fiction that I'd expected.

But, no complaints - truth is often stranger than fiction and I've thoroughly enjoyed doing it all, hopefully anticipating the enjoyment of its readers.

I hadn't come across the basic story until the early 1980s and, although I was immediately intrigued, I could find little more about it at the time. Since then I have discovered more and more, some of it thanks to Geoff Godber-Ford. I was very fortunate to meet him on a number of occasions towards the end of his very full and interesting life - and at first I knew nothing at all of his motorcycling past.

We first met through having a common interest in cycles, Moultons in particular. Both he and Alex Moulton were good examples of how well designed machinery can very enjoyably maintain one's mobility in later life. However, by chance I later mentioned motorcycling, whereupon Geoff's other past came flooding out - and so I started making notes. It was these, together with some of his own writings and articles, that started filling out the real story for me.

Then I was lucky enough to be introduced to Dick Weekes, tucked away in a cottage in Nantgwynant, North Wales, who had met Marjorie Cottle in 1983 when she gave a talk to the West Wales Section of the VMCC about her experiences in 1939 - and he had recorded it all on tape! He describes it as being "... a very sprightly and utterly rivetting performance", depite by then being in her 80s. The long transcript of the recording, done very well by Gill Ferris, has given me much more authentic 'new' material. A very much reduced account was later published in *The Classic MotorCycle,* but I am most grateful to Dick for supplying me with all this 'inside information'.

There were many more gems to be unearthed over the following years. For example, I found Tom Whitton's own account which was published in his local paper in October 1939, and there were many others too, all of which are to be found in the list of References included here.

Walker & Carrick's history of the ISDT was of course an essential resource for me, but motorcycling friends from Holland, Germany and the UK were very helpful too because, thanks mainly to them, copies of the September 1939 issues of *The MotorCycle* and *MotorCycling* in English, the *Motor* in Dutch, *Motociclismo* in Italian and *Das Motorrad* in German were made available and were of great value to me.

All those accounts, together with the advice of friends and experts, have helped me interpolate, deduce and guess how some of the grass-roots competition motorcyclists would have thought and what they may have said back in 1939. How they acted and how they helped their fellow riders is historical fact and so there was no need of fiction in that respect.

Consequently, almost all of those appearing in this book were real people, hopefully portrayed appropriately and in character. Clearly most of their conversations are fictitious, but hopefully plausible, although Marjorie Cottle's talk to the VMCC included quite a few extended and amusing quotations of what she remembers that she and others said at the time, so I have been able to include them.

All the currently known participants are listed on following pages, where the few fictional characters that I have invented for the purposes of continuity are listed in light print, and excused here.

As first explained in the Introduction, Eric and his grandson Andy, were my creations, although Eric had already appeared briefly in 'A Tall Short Story', as had Gustav. Malcolm and Connor were probably unnecessary inventions, but I was having fun at the time.

Lavinda however, had already been created for me in some detail by E. Carey-Riggall. Amusing short tales of the adventures and scrapes of Lavinda and her long-suffering pillion-riding boyfriend Roddy, aboard her 350cc Dot-Bradshaw called Felix, appeared irregularly in *The MotorCycle* from 1925 through to the mid '30s.

Later however, the Dot and its successors had finally been replaced by Felix IV, "...a rather special Ariel Red Hunter - with footchange!" It seemed to me that this modern young lady, riding what was advertised at the time as being 'The Modern Motorcycle', could well have taken it into her head to go over to Germany to watch the fun in August 1939, as in reality did Ruby Bluebell Gibbs. Consequently, she has added some pseudo-authenticity to the tale, as well as just a taste of romance in her 'brief encounter' with Eric. And why not indeed?

(Sadly however, Mortons Media, who have bought the rights to everything published by The MotorCycle, have refused me permission to reproduce the 18 or more tales, despite admitting that they have no intention of doing so themselves. Nevertheless, the charming short stories can still be accessed in other ways.)

So, apart from these few fictional characters, every one of the others really did exist, including the spectators, and all of them actually did everything as described here. Some, including Miriam Anning; J.A.Woodhouse; Stuart Hyslop; Cyril Rowles; W.Waycott; Gerry Dobbs; Pat Gilfinnan; Dave Edda and Ruby Gibbs, nee Slade, were almost certainly there at the time, either as TSRs or spectators, because, although they were not included in the official ISDT Entry List, they were mentioned in others' subsequent accounts.

Similarly, neither 'artistic license' or 'suspension of disbelief' have needed to be invoked as regards either space or time. However, a great deal has had to be left out here of course, and for example the stories of how the Kompressor BMWs, the giant Mercedes-Benz and the rear-engined Auto-Unions were also vigorously campaigned in Britain just before the war make great reading too.

And then, just before publication and quite by luck, a most coincidental article has appeared in Real Classic magazine in which three friends ride some of the '39 ISDT routes on an Ariel and two Matchlesses in 2013. While the article is interesting in its own right, for me it really strikes a chord as, back in 2011, Roger Gwynn and I set out to do a very similar thing on a couple of Ariels. But quite why we didn't succeed is indeed yet another story.

JRB, Spring 2014

DRAMATIS PERSONÆ

ISDT Organisers

General Adolf Hühnlein	Event Organiser and NSKK Korpsführer
Standartenführer Ruhling	Clerk of Course, NSKK
Gruppenführer Emminger	Chief of Staff, NSKK

Colonel Grimm	Luftwaffe
Baron von Falkenhyn	NSU Betriebsführer
Herr Jaeger	Shell Agent in Salzburg & Munich

ISDT Jury

Herr Kraus	President of Organising Committee and Chairman of ISDT Jury
Oberführer Grolmann	NSKK, Germany
Cav. Carlo Manstretta	Italy
P. J. Nortlier	Holland
Major H.R.Watling	Director of Manufacturers' Union, Britain
Tom W. Loughborough	Secretary of A-CU & FICM

British Officials

Major Oldfield	British Entrants Representative
N. Peter O. Bradley	British Trophy Teams Manager
Lt.Colonel Charles V. Bennett	War Office Teams Manager
Peter Chamberlain	A-CU Rep. and *Cyclops, Motor Cycling* reporter
Miss Bunce	A-CU Assistant

Arthur Bourne	Editor of *The MotorCycle*
Graham Walker	Editor of *MotorCycling*

British Competitors

NB each competitor is listed only once, in order of their teams' status

KEY:

Int = International Trophy (teams of 4)   V = International Vase Trophy (teams of 3)
H = Hühnlein Trophy - Military, Police and similar organisatiions (teams of 3)
B = Bowmaker Trophy - Clubs (teams of 3)   M = Manufacturers' Trophy (teams of 3)

TM = Team Manager   TSR = Travelling Support Rider &/or s/c passenger
Res = Reserve   X = Unknown name

CSMA = Civil Service Motoring Ass'n   Sun = Sunbeam MotorCycle Club
ACU = Auto-Cycle Union S.E.Centre   WO = War Office
SC = Sutton Coldfield & N.B'ham MCC   Cov = Coventry & Warwickshire MC
B'ham = Birmingham MCC   Wem = Wembley Speedway MCC
WoE = West of England MCC   Brad = Bradford & District MC
Car = Carshalton MCC   Liv = South Liverpool MC

AJS = A.J.Stevens   Mat = Matchless   (AJS + Matchless = AMC)
Nor = Norton   Tri = Triumph
BSA = Birmingham Small Arms   Ariel = Ariel Motors
Pan = Panther   RE = Royal Enfield

For Example: 'Len Heath V/A, B-Sun/A, M-Ar/A' was competing for the Vase Trophy on behalf of Britain in Team A, for the Bowmaker Trophy on behalf of the Sunbeam Club in Team A and for the Manufacturer's Trophy on behalf of Ariel Motors in Team A.

Comp.No.	Name	Machine	Reg.No.	Teams	Comments
				INTERNATIONAL	
58	Vic Brittain	Norton 490 OHC	FOG 175	Int, B-SC, M-Nor	Clean sheet
135	George Rowley	AJS 347 OHC	FXM 791	Int, B-Car, M-AJS	
52	Allan Jeffries	Triumph 498	EWK 3X	Int, B-Brad, M-Tri	puncture Day2
249	Harold Flook	Norton 596 s/c	FOG 177	Int, B-SC, M-Nor	
TSR	Alec Flook	Norton 596 s/c	FOG 177	Int, B-SC, M-Nor	s/c with Flook
TSR	J. Williams	Norton 350	?	Int, V	
				VASE	
27	Len Heath	Ariel 497	?	V/A, B-Sun/A, M-Ar/A	crashed Day2
81	G.F. Povey	Ariel 497	?	V/A, B-B'ham, M-Ar/A	
128	W.T. (Billy) Tiffen	Velocette 348	?	V/A, B-WoE	Ret'd Day2 split tank
137	Charley Rogers	Royal Enfield 346	CWP 913	V/B, B-Sun/B, M-RE	
108	W.A. West	Ariel 497	EOG 373	V/B, B-Sun/B, M-Ar/A	
121	G.N. Wood	Triumph 343	ERW 498	V/B, B-Brad, M-Tri	
				HÜHNLEIN	
TM	Tom Davies			CSMA	
47	Les Ridgway	BSA 496 M24 Gold St	FOC 776	H-CSMA	Ret'd Day4 hit dog
30	Fred Perks	BSA 496 M23 iron GS	DOV 657	H-CSMA	
14	Fred Whitehouse	BSA 496 M24 Gold St	?	H-CSMA	
TSR	Norman Blockley	BSA 496	?	H-CSMA, M-BSA	bro' of Tim Blockley

No.	Name	Machine	Reg.	Class	Notes
140	Alan Sanders	Triumph 343	?	H-Sun, B-Cov	
255	Marjorie Cottle	Triumph 249	DDU 3?	H-Sun, B-Sun/B	
TSR	Dorothy X	F-B 250	?	H-Sun, B-Sun/B	friend of Cottle
147	Geoff Godber-Ford	Sunbeam 347	FXM 788	H-Sun, B-Sun/B	
TSR	Pat Gilfinnan	Ariel 350	?	H-Sun, B-Sun/B	friend of G G-F
237	X Hitchcock	Triumph 249	?	H-ACU/A	
151	R.R Meier	Triumph 343	?	H-ACU/A	
174	L.E.C Hall	Rudge 499 s/c	KMP 607	H-ACU/A, B-Sun/B	Ret'd Day4
TSR	X X	Rudge 499 s/c	KMP 607	H-ACU/A, B-Sun/B	s/c with Hall
20	H.M. Toomey	Panther 498	?	H-ACU/B, B-Sun/C, B-Pan	Ret'd Day1
87	J.F. Whitfield	BMW 494	?	H-ACU/B	Ret'd Day2
63	Tim Blockley	BSA 496	?	H-ACU/B, B-Sun/C	Ret'd Day3 hit head
	Bert Perrigo	BSA Scout saloon		WO/BSA	BSA Rep for Army Teams
113	Jackie Wood	BSA M24 GoldSt 496	EOG 22	H-WO/A	Private, bent front rim
75	Paddy Doyle	BSA M24 GoldSt 496	EOG 20	H-WO/A	Corporal
101	Fred Rist	BSA M24 GoldSt 496	EOG 21	H-WO/A	Sergeant, Tank Corps
68	J.F. Riley	Norton 490	FOG 856	H-WO/B	Lt., Ret'd Day2 split tank
36	I.T. Dalby	Norton 490	?	H-WO/B	Sergeant, split tank
6	G.M Berry	Norton 490	?	H-WO/B	Corporal, Ret'd Day2 split tank
156	O.G. Davies	Matchless 347	PMF 16	H-WO/C	Sergeant, RASC
131	E. Smith	Matchless 347	PMF 15	H-WO/C	BQMS, Ret'd Day2 hit bus
142	M B.Mackay	Matchless 347	PMF 14	H-WO/C	Sergeant, crashed Day2
Res	Joe Acheson	BSA 496	?	H-WO/A,B,C	Private, didn't ride

BOWMAKER

No.	Name	Machine	Reg.	Class	Notes
160	Jack Breffitt	Norton 348	?	B-SC, M-Nor	Ret'd Day4 bent fork spindle
167	C.R. Bales	BSA 348	?	B-Cov	
152	F.V. Chambers	Royal Enfield 346	?	B-Cov	
163	J.J. Booker	Royal Enfield 346	CWP 912	B-B'ham	
64	Harold Tozer	BSA 496 s/c	FOG 949	B-B'ham, M-BSA	
TSR	X X	BSA 496 s/c		B-B'ham, M-BSA	s/c with Tozer
123	E. Williams	Royal Enfield 346	?	B-Wem	Ret'd Day2
24	W.H.J. Peacock	Ariel 997 s/c	?	B-Wem, M-Ar/B	Ret'd Day1
TSR	X X	Ariel 997 s/c		B-Wem, M-Ar/B	s/c with Peacock
237	J.A. Hitchcock	Triumph 249	?	B-Wem	
125	Tom Whitton	AJS 347	FXM 792	B-WoE, M-AJS	
116	J.H. Amott	BSA 496	FOG 173	B-WoE	
171	R. Wilkinson	Panther 348	?	B-Brad	
87	Jeff Whitfield	BMW 494	?	B-Sun/C	
162	J.S. Botte	Panther 347	?	B-Pan	Ret'd Day3
219	F.H.Whittle	Panther 598	FTO 288	B-Pan	
148	George Eighteen	Matchless 347	FXM 789	B-Car, M-Mat	Ret'd Day3 off bridge
158	Ron Clayton	Triumph 343	?	B-Liv	
39	Graham Oates	Ariel 997 s/c	RKL 399	B-Liv	Ret'd Day1 misfire
TSR	Eric Dale	Scott 600	PSU 754	B-Liv	s/c with Oates
166	Colin Edge	Matchless 347	FXM 790	B-Liv, M-Mat	

185

MANUFACTURERS

TM	Fred Neill			AMC	
222	D.A. Gulliford	AJS 246	?	M-AJS	Ret'd Day1
170	Wag Bennett	Matchless 347	?	M-Mat	
132	Hugh Sim	Triumph 343	EHP 491	M-Tri	
TM	Tom Davies			BSA	
116	Jack Amott	BSA 496	?	M-BSA	
211	J. Ashworth	BSA 249	?	M-BSA	
TM	Ernie Smith	Ariel 997 s/c	?	Ariel	Bob Halliday in s/c
34	Harold Taylor	Ariel 997 s/c	?	M-Ar/B	Ret'd Day2 bent forks
TSR	X X	Ariel 997 s/c		M-Ar/B	s/c with Taylor
92	S.E.(Buster) Cunningham	Ariel 497	?	M-Ar/B., B-Car	
TSR	Vera Cunningham	?	?	M-Ar	
162	J.S. Botte	Panther 349	?	M-Pan	
171	R. Wilkinson	Panther 349	?	M-Pan	
219	F.H.Whittle	Panther 598	FTO 288	M-Pan	
163	Jack Booker	Royal Enfield 346	CWP 912	M-RE	
152	F.V. Chambers	Royal Enfield 346	?	M-RE	

PRIVATE

10	J.B. Croker	Triumph 498	?	Private Entry	
42	T.H. Mooney	Ariel 497	?	Private Entry	
77	Rick Money	BSA 496	?	Private Entry	Lt. R-Eng, Recalled Day4
119	Dr. R.L. Galloway	Rudge 499 s/c	?	Private Entry	Ret'd Day2 s/c detached
TSR	William Galloway	Rudge 499 s/c		Private Entry	s/c with father
127	Jack White	Ariel 348	?	Private Entry	
145	C. Jayne	Royal Enfield 348	?	Private Entry	
155	J.H. Bryant	Ariel 348	?	Private Entry	
274	F. Fletcher	Excelsior 124	?	Private Entry	Ret'd Day2
167	Chris Bates	BSA 348	?	Private Entry	
TSR	Connor X	BSA 348	?	Private Entry	

BRITISH SPECTATORS

Jack Woodhouse	Bentley Coupe	GL 83?	British motorcycle & car dealer, Cologne
Jimmy Simpson	Rover saloon		Shell Agent
Reuben Harveyson	Rover saloon		friend of Simpson and Holliday
Stuart Hyslop	Triumph 600 sv s/c		
Stuart Weycott	Velocette s/c		+ passenger?
Ruby Gibbs	Norton (Works)		very experienced MCC trials rider
TSR? W. Waycott	Velocette 600		
Peggy X	train/car		Edge's fiancé
Miriam Anning	BSA 500 Empire Star		very experienced triallist & ISDT competitor
TSR? Dave Edda	?		friend of G.G-Ford
Cyril Rowles	Matchless 500		
George & Louie McLean	car		
Lavinda Hawsett	Ariel 348		
Malcolm X	BSA 500 s/c		no s/c pass'r

Belgian Competitor

2	van Maldeghem	BMW 597	Private Entry

Bohemian & Moravian Competitor

88	J.Cedik	BMW 495	Private Entry

Swiss Competitor

?	E.Haller	Universal 674 s/c	Private Entry	refs made to competing, but not in Prog

Hungarian Competitors

80	A.Kosma	BMW 495	Private Entry
143	A.van Dory	NSU 346	Private Entry
168	F.Lukavecz	NSU 346	Private Entry
244	X Patho	NSU 562	Private Entry

Dutch Competitors

			VASE	
18	Gerrit de Ridder	BMW 597	V/A, M-BMW	
40	Jaap Fijma	Ariel 497	V/A	competed post-war
70	Jan Moejes	BMW 495	V/A, M-BMW	
32	Dick Renooy	Eysink 350	V/B	
157	Jo Bovee	Velocette 348	V/B	
173	van Rijn	Velocette 348	V/B	

			HÜHNLEIN	
56	Sybrandy	?	H-MCWeO, B-MCWeO	*MCWeO =*
82	v. d.Voort	?	H-MCWeO, B-MCWeO	*M.C.Wassenaar en Omstreken*
229	Herman Zuur	BMW s/c 600	H-MCWeO, B-MCWeO	
TRS XX		BMW s/c 600	H-MCWeO, B-MCWeO	s/c with Zuur

			MANUFACTURERS
97	Piet Knijnenburg	BMW	M-BMW
264	Piet van.Dinter	DKW	M-DKW
269	A.van Dinter	DKW	M-DKW
275	F. Nagtegaal	DKW 125	M-DKW

Swedish Competitors

VASE

9	X.Hedelin	DKW	V, H-SMK	*SMK = ?*
45	X.Larsson	BMW	V, B-AMCN	*AMCN = ?*
78	X.Lindvall	DKW	V, B-SMK	

HÜHNLEIN

21	X.Dahl	?	H-FMCK, B-AMCN
61	X.Lauren	?	H-FMCK, B-SMK
98	X.Nilsson	?	H-FMCK, B-AMCN

German Competitors

INTERNATIONAL

11	Rudi Seltsam	BMW 494	Int	
191	Otto Sensburg	DKW 245	Int, M-AU/A	rode DKW 244 in German team, '54 ISDT
178	Walter Fahler	DKW 250	Int, M-AU/A	rode DKW 244 in German team, '54 ISDT
184	Ludwig Kraus	BMW 596 s/c	Int	aka 'Wiggerl' rode BMW 600 in 1953 ISDT
TSR	Josef Müller	BMW 596 s/c	Int	s/c with Kraus

VASE

35	Josef Forstner	BMW	V/A	
13	Fritz Linhardt	BMW R51	V/A	Oberfeldwebe
38	Hans Lodermeier	BMW	V/A	
49	Julius von Krohn	Zundapp KS600 s/c	V/B, M-Zun	
TSR	X. Durr	Zundapp KS600 s/c	V/B, M-Zun	s/c with von Krohn
104	Josef Hecker	Zundapp KS600 s/c	V/B, M-Zun	
TRS	X.X	Zundapp KS600 s/c	V/B, M-Zun	s/c with Hecker
179	X. Grenz	Zundapp KS600 s/c	V/B, M-Zun	
TSR	X.X	Zundapp KS600 s/c	V/B, M-Zun	s/c with Grenz

The 3 Team B Zundapp outfits were replaced by 3 solos at last minute. No explanation given. Replacements unknown.

HUHNLEIN

17	H. Fruth	BMW 500	H-NSKK/A	*NSKK =*
67	X. Binkhofer, 176 X.Gabriel, XX		H-NSKK/A	*NationalSozialistisches KraftfahrKorps*
110	X. Roese	?	H-NSKK/B, B-NSKKMB/C	Obertruppführer
8	H.Beckhusen		H-NSKK/B, B-NSKKMB/C	*NSKKMB =*
76	O.Beckhusen		H-NSKK/B, B-NSKKMB/C	*Motorgruppe Berlin*
246	G.Ilgenstein	DKW 250	H-NSKK/C	rode Maico 175 in German team, '53 ISDT
248	Schaumburg, 258 Riedel , XX		H-NSKK/C	
206	Berenek, 225 Walz, 230 Suchenek		H-NSKK/D	
4	A.Gruber, 96 Mayer, 204 Drax		H-NSKK/E, B-NSKKMH	*NSKKMH =*
				Motorgruppe Hochland
164	Duckerschein	BMW 600	H-NSKK/F, B-NSKKMB/A	
209	Pusch, 139 Kleff, XX		H-NSKK/F	
99	Sieber, 149 Willnecker, 224 Schottl		H-NSKK/G	
218	Boden	DKW 248	H-NSKK/H	Oberscharführer
187	Groh, 241 Reuuschel , XX		H-NSKK/H	

256	H.Staab	NSU 239	H-NSKK/J, B-NSKKMH	rode NSU 247 in '53 & '54
193	Forster,	232 Treutlein	H-NSKK/J	
217	L.Wolfart	Zundapp 245	H-NSKK/K	Truppführer, fell on gravel
181	Adam,	245 Weigand	H-NSKK/K	
208	Wm.Behrendt	Zundapp 250	H-NSKK/L	
195	Dost,	236 Staschel	H-NSKK/L	
198	Reichenberger, 227 Kussin, 252 Luthardt		H-NSKK/M	

115	Mundhenke, 83 Patina, 5 Denzel	H-SS/A	SS =
207	Low, 221 Rieh, 260 Hainz	H-SS/B	SchutzStaffel
205	Thuring, 223 Leppin, 253 Witteck	H-SS/C	
233	G.Sandkuhler DKW	H-SS/D	
62	Muller, 117 Ehrich	H-SS/D	
25	Zimmermann Zundapp KS500	H-SS/E, B-NSKKSSOM/B	Untersturmführer
153	Weih, 220 Berchthold	H-SS/E, B-NSKKSSOM/B	NSKKSSOM =
74	Fischer, 84 Beinl, 214 Ruthner	H-SS/F	SS Oberabschnitt Main

65	Stolfmann, 100 Maciejewski, 201 Loffler	H-WH/A	WH = ?
54	Wolf, 189 W.Reinhardt, 134 Diez	H-WH/B	

22	Jacobi BMW 500	H-WL/A	minor fall, snapped off cylinder barrel
15	Hoeser, 37 Luber	H-WL/A	
129	Werker, 239 F.Weber, 254 Baumann	H-WL/B	
28	Eitel, 48 Grimm, 86 E.Reinhardt	H-WL/C	WL = ?

31	Sauermann, 71 Klein, 106 Niehoff	H-WM	WM = ?

194	K.Steinberger Zundapp 600	H-DDAC/A	DDAC =
3	Hahmeyer, 202 Charbonier	H-DDAC/A	Der Deutsche Automobil-Club
188	Nowisch, 276 Wirth, 180 Zureck	H-DDAC/B	
			DR=
79	Wiese, 144 Hartwig, 199 Rembowski	H-DR	Deusche Reichspost

BOWMAKER

196	H.Scherzer DKW 245	B-NSKKMS/A, M-AU/C	rode 350 s/c, 1953 ISDT
272	Hermann, 120 Keitel	B-NSKKMS/A	NSKKMS =
187	Groly, 218 Boden, 241 Reuschel	B-NSKKMS/B	Motorgruppe Sachsen

139	Klett ?	B-NSKKMB/A	NSKKMB =
246	Ilgenstein, 248 Schaumburg, 258 Riedel	B-NSKKMB/B	Motorgruppe Berlin

175	Wolfgang Milenkovics Puch 248	B-NSKKMA, M-SDP/A	retired with ignition problems
257	Pogner ?	B-NSKKMA, M-SDP/A	NSKKMA =
235	Waska ?	B-NSKKMA, M-SDP/A	Motorgruppe Alpenland

181	Adam ?	B-NSKKMF/A	NSKKMF =
217	Wolhlfahrt, 245 Weigand	B-NSKKMF/A	Motorgruppe Franken
198	Reichenberger,227 Kussin, 252 Luthardt	B-NSKKMF/B	

206	Beranek, 225 Walz, 230 Suchanek	B-NSKKMO	NSKKMO =
			Motorgruppe Ostmark
			NB Ostmark = Austria

Riders / Bikes	Code	Description
99 Sieber, 149 Willnecker, 224 Schottl	B-NSKKMBO	NSKKMBO = Motorgruppe Bayr.Ostmark
193 Forster, 232 Treutlein	B-NSKKMH	NSKKMH = Motorgruppe Hessen
195 Dost, 208 Behrendt, 236 Staschel	B-NSKKMO	NSKKMO = Motorgruppe Ostland
154 Walter, 94 Dunz, 234 Offlinger	B-NSKKM155/A	NSKKM155 =
138 W. Pieffer, NSU	B-NSKKM155/B, M-NSU/B	Motorsturm 11/M155
165 Eisenmann NSU	B-NSKKM155/B, M-NSU/B	
150 Robert Dollmann NSU 346	B-NSKKM155/B, M-NSU/B	rode NSU Fox 98 in '52
177 A.Weber, 212 Berger, 251 Pauli	B-NSKKM155/C	
5 Wolfgang Denzel BMW 496	B-NSKKSSOD	rode Puch in Austrian team, '50 ISDT
115 Mundhenke, 83 Patina	B-NSKKSSOD	NSKKSSOD = SS Oberabschnitt Donau
207 Low Triumph 250	B-NSKKSSOM/A	NSKKSSOM =
260 Hainz Triumph 250	B-NSKKSSOM/A	SS Oberabschnitt Main
221 Riess ?	B-NSKKSSOM/A	
74 Fischer, 84 Beinl, 214 Ruthner	B-NSKKSSSDF	B-NSKKSSSDF = SS Standarte 'Der Furer"
62 Muller, 117 Ehrich, 233 Sandkuhler	B-NSKKSSLAH	NSKKSSLAH = SS Leibstandarte 'Adolf Hitler'
216 Cymral, 238 Uray, 250 Gunther	B-NSKKSSOA	NSKKSSOA = SS Oberabschnitt Alpenland
44 K.Dobereiner BMW 750 s/c	B-DDACGH	
TSR X.X BMW 750 s/c	B-DDACGH	s/c with Dobereiner
114 Feick, 159 Peterssohn	B-DDACGH	DDACGH = DDAC Gau Hessen
202 Charbonier, 243 Pohl, 268 Eisner	B-DDACOW	DDACOW = DDAC Ortsgruppe Wernigerode
194 Steinberger, 3 Hahmayer, 133 Kohler	B-DDACOM	DDACOM = DDAC Ortsgruppe Munchen

MANUFACTURERS

Riders / Bikes	Code	Description
250 P.Gunther Puch	M-SDP/B	SDP =
238 Uray, 216 Cmyral	M-SDP/B	Steyr-Daimler-Puch A-G
130 G.Doiterweich Victoria 342	M-Vic	Vic =
126 Hasselbeck Victoria	M-Vic	Victoria-Werke A-G
161 Marx Victoria	M-Vic	

146 Ishinger	DKW	M-AU/A	*AU =*
277 H.Walter, 272 Hermann, 268 Eisner		M-AU/B	*Auto Union A-G*
243 Ullrich Pohl	Maico 173	M-AU/C	rode Maico & DKW 245 in 1952,'53 & '54
182 Demelbauer	?	M-AU/C	
136 H.Kirchberg	DKW 343	M-AU/D	
133 Kohler, 120 Keitel		M-AU/D	
154 Faron Walter	NSU 600 s/c	M-NSU/A	*NSU = NSU Werke*
TSR X.X	NSU 600 s/c	M-NSU/A	s/c with Walter
94 Dunz	NSU 600 s/c	M-NSU/A	SS
TSR X.X	NSU 600 s/c	M-NSU/A	s/c with Dunz
234 Oettinger	NSU 600 s/c	M-NSU/A	Oberscharführer
TSR X.X	NSU 600 s/c	M-NSU/A	s/c with Oettinger
177 A.Weber	NSU 242	M-NSU/C	
212 Berger,	NSU 242	M-NSU/C	
251 Pauli	NSU 242	M-NSU/C	

PRIVATE

266 K.Kneiss	Hercules-Sachs	Private Entry	rode Express 173 in 1953 ISDT
?? A.v.Falkenhaysen	BMW 500	Private Entry	competed, but not listed in Programme
226 H.Thumshirn	Ardie 250	Private Entry	sponsored by Ardie-Werke?
53 S.Luck	BMW 494	Private Entry	

Italian Competitors

INTERNATIONAL

12 Serafini	Gilera 500	Int, M-FMG	
7 Grieco	Gilera 500	Int, M-SAFA/A	
203 Gilera	Sertum 250	Int	
124 Villa	Gilera s/c 600	Int	
TSR X.X	Gilera s/c 600	Int	s/c with Villa

VASE

215 Francone	Sertum	V/A, M-SAFA/B
231 Brunetto	Sertum	V/A, M-SAFA/A
16 Benzoni	Sertum	V/A, M-SAFA/A
247 Ramazzotti	Guzzi	V/B
19 Ventura	Gilera	V/B
26 Cavanna	Mas	V/B

HÜHNLEIN

33 Nocchi, 50 Ascari, 55 Palvis ???	H-MDS/A	*MDS = ?*
66 Sbaragli, 72 Bandirola, 85 Bernardoni	H-MDS/B	
90 Agostinelli, 95 Scatolini, 102 Mangione	H-MDS/C	
24 Cavaciuti, 74 Clememcich, 111 Sanvito	H-MVSN/A	*MVSN = ?*
44 Panella, 105 Micheli, 261 Francisci	H-MVSN/B	

60	Conficoni, 93 Bellavita, 118 Lama		H-MVSN/C	
			MANUFACTURERS	
12	Ettore	Gilera	M-MFG	*FMG =*
124	Gilera	Gilera	M-MFG	*Fabrica Motocicli Gilera*
107	Fornasari, 259 Zanella ??		M-SAFA/B	*SAFA =*
				S.A. Fauso Alberi

ACKNOWLEDGEMENTS & THANKS
- to those who have helped in the writing this book

Geoff Godber-Ford for talking to me at such great length and answering so many questions on a number of different occasions.

Dick Weekes for lending me his tape of Marjorie Cottle's talk to the VMCC, to Jane Pickard for introducing me to him and to Gill Ferris for transcribing it all.

Cyril Ayton, the original Editor of *MotorCycle Sport*, who took a keen interest throughout, recalling interesting facts about some of those involved and disinterring some of his Blue and Green 'Uns from 1939 for me.

Pat Robotham, my erstwhile MCC mentor, who also took an interest - and introduced me to Lavinda.

Speedtracktales website, a wonderful source of information about the ISDTs, with useful links thanks to webmaster Adrian's help.

The Motoring Research Service at the National Motor Museum, Beaulieu, and the Vintage MotorCycle Club Library at Allen House, Burton Upon Trent, and to Dave Giles who helped me there.

In addition, I also greatly appreciate the help also given by, amongst others, Annie McGregor for encouragement; Brian Cowper for artwork; Bill Snelling for photographs and advice; Paul Jameson for materials; John Prince for translations, Dr. Robert Poole for checking the history; Peter Henshaw, Jim Reynolds, Roger Gwynn and Herman Noort for additional facts and constructive comments, and both Ann Livesley and Gill Ferris for final proof reading.

However, despite all this help, any further misinterpretations, mistakes, or other errors that have survived can now only be laid at the author's door.

REFERENCES
- as published, in chronological order

Specifically Concerning the 1939 ISDT :

The International - A Dramatic Climax   TM-C Reporter
                                               TM-C, Aug 31st, 1939

La XXi Sei Gioni Internazionale   Gino Magnani
                                               MCicli, Aug & Sept, 1939

XXI Internalionale Sechstagefaht   Gustav Mueller
                                               DM, Sept 2nd, 1939

Sent Home From Germany   David Whitton
an interview of Tom Whitton   MDA, Sept, 1939

Prisoners of the Gestapo!   F. Bates & F. Gwilliam
an account of a European tour   MC, Oct, 1939

How German Militarism Misused A Great Event Peter Chamberlain
Parts 1&2   MC, Jan 8th &15th, 1942

The Marjorie Cottle Tape   Marjorie Cottle
talk to VMCC   unpublished   1983

Six Day Stories   Bob Halliday
Parts 1&2   MCI, June & July, 1966

The Pre-War Internationals   Titch Allen
Parts 1&2   MCS, Oct. & Sept. 1968

Marjorie: Queen of Trials   John Brown
the story of Marjorie Cottle   TCM-C Feb. & Apr. 1982

Trials - and Success!   Ivan Taylor
the story of Geoff Godber-Ford   TCM-C, February, 1984

It Was 'Different' All Right   Patrick Click
an interview of Fred Perks   TCM-C, December, 1984

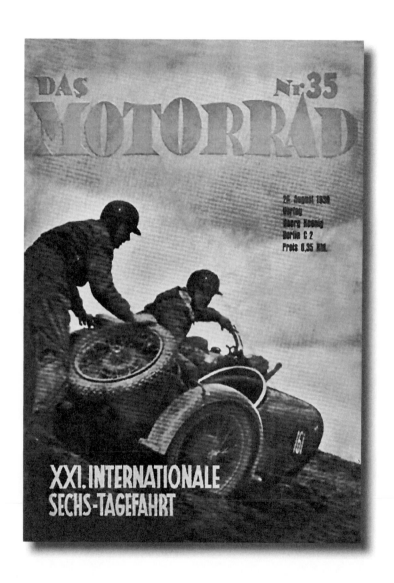

DAS MOTORRAD

Nr. 35

26. August 1936
Verlag
Georg Koenig
Berlin C 2
Preis 0,35 RM.

XXI. INTERNATIONALE SECHS-TAGEFAHRT

International Six-Days Trial
the history of the ISDT

M.Walker & R.Carrick
pub Osprey, 1992

Aurora to Ariel
biography of Graham Oates

Bill Snelling
pub Amulree, 1993

Cheating Hitler

Geoff Godber-Ford
MCS&L, July, 1997

An Interesting Life!

Geoff Godber-Ford
TN-IN, Dec, 1997

The Day That War Broke Out

Ken Hallworth
TCM-C, December, 2009

21 Internationale Sechstagefahrt
original NSU promo film - DVD

NSU
pub Audi Tradition, 2010

A Great Escape
a re-run of some of the routes

John Tinley
RC, May 2014

ISDT 1939 - Germany

Speed Track Tales
www.speedtracktales.com/index-of-isdt-events/isdt-1939-germany

DM	Das Motorrad
MCicli	MotoCiclismo
MC	Motor Cycling
MCS	MotorCycle Sport
MCS&L	MCS & Leisure
MDA	Mid Devon Advertiser
RC	Real Classic
TM-C	The Motor-Cycle
TCM-C	The Classic Motor-Cycle
TN-IN	The New-Imperial News

Concerning Relevant Pre-War Situations :

Tourist Trophy Number

TM-C Reporters
TM-C, June, 1939

Racing the Silver Arrows
Mercedes-Benz vs Auto-Union, 1934 to 1939

Chris Nixon
Osprey, 1996

Hitler's Grand Prix in England
Donnington 1937 & 1938

Christopher Hilton
Haynes, 1999

Guilty Victim
Austria: from the Holocaust to Haider

Hella Pick
pub I.B. Taurus, 2000

The Third Reich in Power
the diary of an American journalist in Berlin, 1939

Richard J Evans
Penguin, 2006

The Nazi TT
Hitler's 1939 propoganda victory on the IoM

Roger Willis
Motobusiness, 2009

About the Author

John Bradshaw grew up surrounded by mechanical things and has not escaped so far. He has always owned wheels and currently has a stable ranging from an 1880s Cogent Ordinary bicycle to a modified 1990s BMW R1200C, with Ariel, Land-Rover, Morgan, Moulton, Pedersen & Scott in between. Nothing very modern though, as it couldn't be fixed.

He was the Social-Secretary and then Chairman of the Ariel Owners MotorCycle Club in the 1980s and then created and for a decade ran *CycleFest*, an international alternative cycle event.

He was the editor of a Mathematical Asssociation journal for many years and has also written articles for a variety of cycling, motorcycling and motoring magazines, still occasionally doing so.

Despite having toured and occasionally sprinted and hill-climbed motorcycles, he only belatedly rediscovered the MCC and now regularly competes in a 1973 Morgan 4/4 (much modified in an attempt to compensate for its driver's inadequacy), while wishing that he'd started many years earlier - on his Ariel.

Also by JRB:

Square Forum (with Ralph Hawkins)
Mathematics and Art (with Leslie Jones)
Ariels And Their Owners
CJKB – Colin Bradshaw's biography
Transmogrification
A Tall Short Story
The Artful Bodger (with Peter Henshaw)
ODTAA
Horsing About - Jo Newell's biography
Ordinary